SIX-POINTER BUCK

SIX-POINTER BUCK

David Stephen

C

CENTURY PUBLISHING

LONDON

For Jess
and the happy years with
Bounce and Sanshach

First published in Great Britain in 1956 by
Lutterworth Press

This edition published in 1985 by
Century Publishing Co. Ltd,
Portland House, 12–13 Greek Street,
London W1V 5LE

ISBN 0 7126 0820 6

Printed in Great Britain by
Photobooks (Bristol) Ltd

I

THE SHORT SUMMER DARKNESS HAD KNOWN NO SOUND but the purr and swish of rain. Daybreak came with a freshening wind and the wet trees dripping. Rifting clouds drew away to north and south, and star clusters flickered in the widening arch of the sky. With the first pale light in the east, unseen swifts screamed overhead on scimitar wings to greet the dawn.

The doe stood under the trembling hazels on the fringe of Glencryan, with head up and ears forward, facing the brightening east. Since the rain ceased at the darkest hour she had stood there, toeing the earth lightly with one hindfoot while resting heavily on the other, moving only to shift her weight or nose nervously at her flank. This was her feeding hour, but she had no craving for food; no urge to join the proud six-pointer buck grazing in the murky ground twilight with her twin yearling fawns. She had grown suddenly weary of his company. Even the yearlings irked her. Jaded, leg-weary, and heavy with the new life thrusting at her flanks, she longed for solitude; for the secret place among the birches on Heatherfield Common where all her fawns had first seen the light of day.

A swirl of wind ruffled the hazels, scattering gathered rain. A trickle dropped on the erect ears of the doe, making her reach for a branch to rub out the itch of water. The movement brought down a greater shower and a fat drop found her eyes. She kicked with a hindfoot, shaking her head, but the annoyance in her ears was as commanding as ever. She rubbed an ear against the inside of her knee. The relief was instant and satisfying, so she drew in her leg, put the other foot forward, and repeated the rubbing with her second ear. With a final shake of her head, she replaced the foot in its slot, then readjusted her weight. When she turned to gaze through the hazel screen again she had not changed her original stance.

Tenuous waves of pink were now washing over the spreading pallor in the eastern sky, and a thin line of flaming gold edged the black, serried velvet of the distant pines. The far sky became luminous, clear as a thrush's egg; trees and knowes and butts, no longer occluded, took shape in the lessening twilight over the heather. Wisps and streamers of white cloud, drifting above the dawn light, were flushed with palest rose-pink and saffron, and the herald star faded in the greater radiance.

Grouse chuckled and challenged when the doe could see her feet in the shrinking shadows under the hazels. The sun came up with spears and banners of fire, spreading a fan of light across the moor, and touching the remotest cloud tassels with its far-flung flames. A hawk-like bird, with barred breast and long tail, pitched in a shaggy pine behind the doe, where it perched like an owl, with two toes in front and two behind. The bird called *cuc-cu-koo*, then hissed and bubbled, inflating its throat. It stuttered its triple call a second time before flying away across the heather with a little bird in pursuit.

The grazing buck threw up his antlered head when the cuckoo passed over. At that moment the first larks sang and a cock pheasant crowed in the deep of the heather. The doe backed slowly through the hazels, shaking down a shower of raindrops brilliant with reflected skylight. Her time had come. Clear of the hazels, she turned quickly but stealthily, and leaped the wide, blaeberry-lipped ditch into the floodlit vistas of Glencryan.

Beside an ancient pine, with cracked and fissured bark

6

blood-red in the sunrise, she paused to look back, as though reluctant to leave the little herd. She was now too far out to hear the rip of cropped grass, but her sensitive nose placed the trio still grazing on the moor-edge sward. Her stealthy withdrawal had not been noticed.

Avoiding her usual runways, perhaps to escape the buck should he attempt to follow, she turned into the pines, trotting through drenched blaeberries and soaking grass till she reached the massed willows at the boundary fence. Beyond was a wide channel of shining green—sphagnum moss covering a long depression which drained the moor and fed the Glencryan burn with peat-filtered water. Foxes avoided the treacherous, spongy carpet, from which cows had more than once been pulled after sinking to the udder, but the roe had a subtler sense of ground than any fox, and a wariness alien to any cow. She went on without hesitation.

The squelchy sphagnum sucked her in to the fetlocks at the first step, oozing black and blue oily water with a milky scum, but she displayed no sign of fear. Her next step took her on to a rush clump, which gave her firm foothold on the quaking green. And of such were her stepping stones. From rush clump to grass cushion and mossed stump she stepped and jumped with hardly a pause, to reach the heather unsoiled above the fetlocks.

A stoat barred her path as she breasted the high, rain-sparkling heather. His belly fur was bedraggled, and his fine squirrel tail sleeked to rat size with wetness. The doe stopped, startled, and tapped petulantly with a forehoof. She had no fear of stoats, and his truculent hiss and chatter merely roused her gentle heart to anger. Her second hoof-tap held unmistakable menace. The stoat's first answer was to uncover needle teeth and show his gums; but he recoiled, with forepaws raised, when the doe minced forward. When she struck out with a foot he

7

darted behind a heather clump, with rump arched and tail held rigid; and there he fumed in silence till she passed on her way.

The snarling of crows greeted her as she left the heather to take a trailless route through the Glencryan beeches. Both snarlers were cocks from Glencryan nests, squabbling over the remains of a young rabbit, defiled by the stoat the doe had just threatened. The muscular boles of the great beeches were touched with glowing pink, veined with black where rain had trickled. Their long shadows lay aslant the brown leaf carpet in parallel rows, with heads hidden in the projected leaf quiver. A woodcock rose in wavering flight where the beeches gave way to pines and birches, and an owl, in identical plumage, with white beads on wings, swept into a great horse chestnut where three owlets sat slit-eyed among the six-fingered fronds. It was then the doe saw the buck and fawns—in line abreast among the pines ahead.

They had found her by chance, after travelling at speed for some distance along their favoured route and giving up the search. The buck, perhaps realizing why she had disappeared, had forked right from the trail to cut through the second pine neck of Glencryan. He had a lie, or harbour, in a hardwood strip beside the ruins of Braeburn Farm which he had used only twice since shedding velvet. He was bound thither when he got the doe's scent on the wind, and had waited for her to come on. The nose that found her on the wind could never have tracked her foot scent; nor had the buck any thought of trying when he discovered she had quit the hazels. Keen though his scenting powers were, his nose depended entirely on wind-borne tidings; foot tracking was for the hunters—the foxes and stoats and weasels—who had the same wind wisdom, and so were doubly blessed.

The doe came right up to the waiting trio, turning

away only when the buck touched her gently on the side of the neck with the prongs of his antlers. He touched her a second time, reaching under her neck with a sideways movement of his head, but again she stepped away, this time with a hint of anger. When the fawns crowded her she stamped with a foot, like a ewe that fears for her lamb. The fawns, accepting her rebuff, nibbled blaeberries without enthusiasm, while the buck, with ears up, stared intently at the doe.

Suddenly, all four deer threw up their heads when a homing fox came trotting light-footed across the tree shadows. He had caked blood on his whiskers and half a rabbit in his belly. The deer hadn't scented him because he came from downwind, which meant he was travelling with the wind on his nose. That was his way of keeping informed about what lay ahead. So he knew about the deer while he was some way off, though they only learned about his coming when his long shadow bobbed along in front of their feet. The fox was wet after his morning prowl, with raggled brush and fur plastered to his ribs. After a disdainful sniff, and assuming a casual air, he sat down with lolling tongue to consider the scene.

Fire kindled in the buck's eyes, while the doe stood at gaze with the fawns hustling her from behind. The buck dreaded no fox, but he trusted none. He was set for war. But the fox had no thought of serious trouble; gorged, and heavy of stomach, he was in expansive mood, with a mind to improve his knowledge of the whimsical roe. He had some knowledge already, for he had once killed a dappled fawn and felt the knife edge of a doe's hoof on his ribs. He was lucky enough to get away without broken bones, but not without a reminder, and the skin was still puckered over the wound. He had no stomach for further experiences of a like nature, so, when the buck wheeled, gouging up a molehill of pine needles with his hooves, he changed his mind about watching and sauntered off with a great show of indifference.

When the fox had gone, with his sly grin and stiff whiskers, the roe moved at leisurely pace through the pines and heather clumps and birch thickets, in single file with the doe leading. On the west fringe of Glencryan, where elders and flowering thorns overhung the crumbling drystane dyke, the doe halted suddenly to rub ear against shoulder. She licked her knee, touched nose to flank, then lay down between a spindly scrub oak and a grass-grown moleheap ringed with bluebells. Buck and fawns couched close by, where branch shadows screened them and fingered their red coats. Settled, they started to chew the cud. The doe, facing her rump, closed her eyes in sleep.

Late that afternoon, when the shadows lay hard and still in sunlight and all four deer had a halo of flies, the buck went to drink from the ditch under the elders. In the shade of the mossy dyke the water was cool. The buck sucked with flies crowding his eyes, kicking at clegs on his belly while the water showed as moving bulges on the satin skin of his gullet. The lift of his head was leisurely, and he stepped back with water dripping from champing jaws. But the instant his head was up his demeanour changed. The chewing jaw movement ceased abruptly. The head twitched and froze; the ears shot up to alert and the neck went rigid; the body became poised for flight, with every muscle taut. Dilated nostrils intercepted the wind's message, and the message read M-A-N!

Two minutes passed, with the buck tense from ears to fetlocks. Unheeded flies crowded his eyelids. The drooping elders, trembling in the wind, foiled his vision, but he held his pose, with straining ears, unwinking eyes, and twitching nostrils. His eyes needed no clear view when the message came so plainly to his nose. But he was uneasy, and waited, framed between over-arching elders, with head and shoulders showing above the dyke.

The man in the woodside ditch, a hundred and twenty yards away, could see the deer's neck, sheened and foxy red in the sun glare. He had seen the buck approaching the dyke and was hoping he would come into the open. But as the minutes slipped away, with the buck alert and unmoving, he lifted his ·22 rifle and methodically adjusted the sights. It came to him suddenly that he was upwind of his quarry; that the deer was watching, not in doubt, but in certain knowledge of his presence. The beast might break away at any moment; he would certainly not come forward into the tainted wind. And no hunter's trick would succeed in making his informed nose take second place to curiosity, for curiosity is born of uncertainty.

Laying the black rifle barrel on an embedded stone, the man put cheek to stock, and lined the sights in his eye. The distance was great and the target small—a neck, and a thin line of shoulder—but the man had no qualms about wounding. And he was using high velocity shells. His squeeze on the trigger was even and steady; there was no last minute tremor of barrel or sights; the empty shell-case shot out at the recoil, and the bullet sped to its target.

The wicked slap of the rifle sent the cushats up in alarm; it came back from the dyke with a smack like a whiplash, and the echoes rattled in Glencryan. Crows barked and fled, and a cock pheasant bolted, head down, through the heather. The buck leaped into the air, turned almost in the same movement, and bounded into the wood, with blood oozing from his neck where the hard-nosed bullet had ploughed a red furrow. Doe and fawns broke cover to the right, careering wildly across the open heather. *Whack-whack-wheeack!* When three snap shots whipped at the fleeing deer failed to strike the man raced to the dyke to look for the buck. He was good enough to know the bullet had not gone past.

But the buck was in the scrub beyond the beeches when the hunter reached the ground furrowed by his take-off. Terrified, but not mortally wounded, he kept up his headlong flight till he reached Braeburn Strip, with its cool shadows and friendly cover. And there he spent the night, without heeding the wound on his neck, or breaking harbour to feed at dusk.

Doe and fawns crossed the last belt of heather at speed, slowing down to a walk when they reached the rough, hillocky pasture beyond the scattered birches, where two crows, strutting with semi-circle swagger, were searching for young pewits in the grass. Their bright eyes, fierce under flat crowns, watched the deer, but they let them pass without comment. Cud-chewing cows, lying chin deep in buttercups, stared and snorted without rising, but three heifers and a snub-horned bull calf trotted after them with screwed tails, to hustle them to the dividing hedge. Seeing no way through the thorns, the doe jumped over the slung birch poles which acted as a gate. The yearlings followed on her heels, clearing the flaking poles with greater ease, and all three walked through the next field in line ahead.

At the field bottom, where the Glencryan burn made a dog-leg turn between high banks overhung with gorse and dogrose, the doe turned left along the hedge to a dunged pathway leading to the water. The deer drank thirstily under clouds of midges, then crossed the burn with the current pulling at their slim legs. On the brae face beyond was a heart-shaped planting of young larches, netted round against rabbits. The yard-high netting was no obstacle to deer. The roe jumped over without halting to test the wind, for it was full on their muzzles and breathed no scent of peril.

Lying under the feathery larches, a few yards apart, they soon forgot their fear. The yearlings recovered more quickly, and completely, because they had no secret excitements. Presently they sprang to their feet to nibble tentatively at curled larch branchlets, while the doe's exposed flank dimpled and palpitated from recent exertion and approaching travail. Her eyes, now heavy of lid, had lost their limpid brilliance. The white Cupid's bow on her upper lip was discoloured with viscid spittle, which her restless tongue could not remove after much licking. Couching in the Heatherfield birches was now a matter of urgency. Though the larch planting had all the heavy cover beloved by roe, she seldom lay up in it. She preferred other thickets, and each May or June found her at Heatherfield, where she had dropped many fawns in other years.

The yearlings lipped larch branchlets without eating, then turned away to nibble at belly-high grass instead. Both nipped off tops, but dropped the bite without chewing. At the moment they had no craving for larch tips, or long, rank grass. Ignoring the doe, they sailed effortlessly over the netting barrier to graze in the field, butting playfully at each other till they were a score of bounds from the wood edge. The doe pricked her ears, and watched.

She was ready to go—without the yearlings. They had no place in her present plans. And she was prepared to drive them away forcibly if need be. Rising wearily, she edged back through the larches, with her eyes on the feeding twins, and her nose hearkening to the wind on her flag. When she was completely hidden from the yearlings, she turned about and picked her way furtively to the far end of the wood.

The sun was now going down in flames, as it had risen, with lilac, violet and purple cloud streamers, outlined in fiery gold, piled low on the horizon. The doe left the wood as a tawny owl, on wings as noiseless as sleep, flapped slowly down the netted edge in search of mice. Peewits curled down to earth, calling *wee-wit* in vibrant voices, because they feared for their chicks, knowing she might trample what she could not see. But they did not assault her, being content to stand guard over their young, ready to turn her with noisy display if she trod on dangerous ground.

The doe gave no thought to the peewits, avoiding them as a matter of course, because it was not her habit to intrude on the privacy of any bird. She might, indeed, have trodden upon a squatting chick or an unguarded nest, and the peewits knew it. They had more understanding of deer and cows and horses than the hoofed beasts had of nesting birds. A fox, or any hunter, they would have attacked with contumely; with deer, as with sheep and cows, they were content to stand guard against friendly, but dangerous, feet.

For a mile the doe travelled at a steady trot—a gait not greatly favoured by her kind; but a walk was too slow to please her mood, and a faster pace unsuited to her condition. A field-length short of Stane Farm, ringed with tall beeches, she turned north, downhill, and crossed the Glencryan burn into a thickly wooded hollow, which was an established meeting place of roe—a junction and crossroads of many trails. There, parties often mixed. Some lay up in it from time to time, and always there was much coming and going in the quiet of nightfall and dawn. There were two breaks on to the road, much used by deer; one at a wrecked and splintered gate, the other at a fence-high bank between tall birches. Tradition had no name for the wood in the hollow, though it was the centre of their world for many deer, and had many trees with roots reaching back far into history.

Opposite the Wood-of-no-name, the road was flanked with oak and ash, elm and beech, twin limes and a solitary, stately larch; behind, the ground fell away steeply to the wide, fast-flowing Luggie Water. Trees clothed the treacherous steep to the burnside levels— elms, widely skirted and shaggy of crown; native Scots pines, tall and muscular, that had known the storms of a hundred winters; larches that feathered the sky with shimmering tops; and immense, spreading horse chestnuts lit with terraced candles.

Down on the level, its pink walls, and straggling roses, and green-painted rain barrel hidden by a thick, dusty planting of spruce and larch, was Fin-me-oot Cottage, where house martins flocked to nest in summer, and small birds found plenteous food on the bird tables when winter came with its frost and snow. There, way-wise deer went in the windy autumn dawns to bite at fallen apples in the little orchard; and there dwelt Patrick MacPherson, red-bearded and wrinkled of face, an Irish-Scot as ever was, with bright owl-like eyes and neither brogue nor blarney.

The doe left the Wood-of-no-name by the broken gate. She went down the slope on a slant, which was not her usual way, furrowing and slotting the wet mould, pressing a faint imprint on the sparse, springy turf, and snipping off bluebell clusters when stems were caught in the cleft of her hooves.

Patrick, watching the sunset from his door, saw her when she came on to the bank a hundred yards downstream, but lost her almost at once when she lowered her head and disappeared under low-reaching alders. With the sun glare full in her eyes she hurried through the bank tangles to the bridge, reaching it as a red bus passed over with a whine of tyres on the smooth surface. She had chosen the burn route to avoid crossing the road, where she had once been caught in headlamps, and where many roe had been killed or maimed by long-distance lorries in the dark.

Crossing the burn where wild liquorice reached up to her belly, she splashed under the bridge in water above her hocks, coming out on the other side beside a grey post that was a heron. A vole turned back from midstream, scuttering over shallows to its burrow under comfrey on the bank, and the heron, waiting to spear it, left because the deer had spoiled her hunting. The doe climbed the slope without looking back, keeping under cover of the scrub oaks and birches and bracken and woodrush till she reached the top. Near the hedge she swerved from a brushwood heap that reeked of fox. A moment's pause at the cornfield hedge, and she jumped it from a standing start.

Rabbits fanning out into the young corn sat up with erect ears when she passed through the line, then fell to nibbling green shoots, unaware that a fox was lying beyond the hedge studying wind and layout. With four fields to go, the doe slowed to a walk, moving with sudden wariness. On the edge of Heatherfield Common, which had once been a great wood, she paused, indistinct in the failing light, to question the wind.

And when the blue-violet dusk was settling, soft and earth-scented, she crossed the rough levels to her chosen sanctuary.

— 2 —

WILD ANIMALS HAVE MANY SECRETS STUBBORNLY KEPT and reluctantly betrayed, and birth and death are the greatest secrets of all. Many are born and many die; and some are seen in the morning of life and some after death by violence; but the act of birth is performed in secret, and death in the fulness of time takes place in seclusion. So the roe seeks a hidden place to drop her fawns, conscious of her own temporary helplessness, and the greater, and more prolonged, helplessness of her young; and the dying animal, understanding nothing of death, but knowing the penalty of weakness in the face of strength, seeks sanctuary in its final hour.

But the weakness of a mother is fleeting, and fear for self becomes a greater fear for the safety of her young, with inaccessibility the guiding impulse and instinctive aim. Many choose the friendly earth as sanctuary—cairn, and cave, and burrow, and dyke, and sheltering shelf. Thus the fox and badger, and the wildcat and rabbit and marten and stoat; and the weasel and hedgehog and mole; and most of the lesser beasts. But a few choose the earth's surface, with their nurseries open to the sky, or perhaps under a screen of trees. And thus the red deer and the roe, and the hares of mountain and valley. And they achieve inaccessibility by remoteness, or dark thickets, or concealing mimicry, separately or in combination; and keep their nurseries inviolate by a stealthy approach, made under cover of darkness if danger threatens by day.

17

The roe chose the Heatherfield birches, covering an elliptical five acres in the middle of the common, because they were seldom visited by human beings, and she had not been molested there in four successive summers.

Though not remote—being in full view of four farms and a highway—the thicket was not easy of access. The surrounding ground was peat on rock, thickly grown over with heather and birch seedlings, firm to the tread; but beyond, in a greater ellipse, was a wide belt of boggy ground, criss-crossed by rush-choked ditches in which pheasants lost many chicks each year. Getting through the bog cotton and rush beds was difficult, fraught with no little risk; horses, bogged down in it, had been shot because they could not be extricated. But the doe had at least two routes through it, by which she could reach the birches without getting wet above the fetlocks.

Two fawns were born in the birch roundel between dusk and morning twilight, while the star Altair, the eye of the eagle, hard and glittering, winked icily from its lofty pitch in the eastern sky. In the tremulous dawn, all moist wind and leaf whisper and water song in the ditches, the doe emerged from the thicket with lowered head and halting steps. Ragged clouds raced towards the sunrise, rose-tinted where the stars were paling, violet and smoky blue in the rain-washed sky to the west. The deer came out with the wind at her back, so that her questioning nostrils could keep watch on her hidden fawns; her mouth was dry and glutty and she wanted to drink.

Rushes, in close canopy, hid the first running water, but she pressed her muzzle against the pleated mass, forced her way through, and shook her head to enlarge the opening. She drank hastily and noisily, with forelegs splayed out and forward, her waving ears acting for her nose. A cock crowed, and she continued sucking; but when a lorry back-fired on the mile-distant highway, she threw up her head in startled question. With lips dripping water she faced the road, cupping her black-edged ears. Upwards, forward and sideways she directed them, independently and together, but cock crow and the far yapping of dogs were all she could catch on the wind. So she lowered her head to drink again, with a sound between a sob and a sigh. Then she turned to go back to the birches.

A few paces from the ditch she stopped abruptly, and reached down to the purple moor grass at her feet. As if suddenly discovering hunger, she started to snatch at the tufted heads. But her cropping was perfunctory, and she didn't turn back when she had grazed to the end of the patch.

She entered the birches as a nightjar, a shadowy swallow garbed like an owl, wavered past on silent wings to its roost among the pines on the ridge two hundred yards away to the south. It called *coo-ic* twice before it reached the trees, and the doe heard its soft churring before it pitched. In the morning twilight it had wheeled and twisted above the common, hawking moths and flies while the owls hunted voles and mice; and now, owl-like, it was flying home to perch lengthwise on its low pine branch, like a piece of dead bark, till the hunting hour of dusk.

When the sun was an hour gold, and the first swallows cleft the air, the doe was standing knee deep among white, scented woodruff, on the fringe of a little clearing, with leaf shadows dappling her coat and a third fawn at her feet. He was a buck fawn, an awkward bundle of sprawling legs, and the doe had just licked him dry.

In giving birth to three fawns she had departed from the usual custom of her kind, for, with the roe deer, twins are normal; but it is unlikely that she gave any thought to the matter, or realised that her present family was in any way different from the others. Numbers meant nothing to her in her pride of motherhood. Two fawns or three—they were a delight to her eyes; so she gave to her last born, the only buck among them, the same gentle care that she had lavished on the others. And he, contrary to the usual rule in big families, was the biggest fawn of them all.

The clearing where the doe had her fawns was shut in on three sides by a peat bank in the shape of a horseshoe, grassed on top and yellow-starred on the face with tormentil and stonecrop. Birches crowded the bank top, and sealed the open end of the horseshow where the buck fawn lay on his woodruff bed. Heather straggled into the clearing, which was a flat outcrop of rock, thinly covered with dark, peaty soil, cracked and furrowed in the pattern of pine bark. Water drained away quickly from the surface into the fissures in the rock beneath, and no birch seedling had ever survived beyond the height of a newly born roe.

Leaving the little buck, the doe walked across the clearing with precise steps and slouching shoulders, to the right-hand curve of the horseshoe, where her other fawns were lying. Couched close to the bank, ten feet apart, they were exposed but not conspicuous, for their white-spotted chestnut coats favoured the brown earth with its trembling leaf shadows and dancing highlights. Both lay chin to ground, with slim legs gathered under them, and their big, soft eyes staring in wonder. At the doe's approach they struggled to rise, but when she touched each in turn with her muzzle they lay still, as if the gesture conveyed command. When she had licked them both, she left without allowing them to nurse.

She wanted to explore the entire birch thicket, to reassure herself that no danger lurked there to threaten her fawns. No twig snapped under her sharp hooves as she picked her way stealthily through the close-set trees. The ground was broken, hillocky, and much cut up by ditches, with heather on the knowes and rank grass in the damp hollows. Greasy and decaying stumps, mossed and grass-grown, were all that remained of the once great wood that had sheltered capercaillie and badger, jay, squirrel and woodpecker. On one of the stumps, which was ringed with purple, white-edged fungus, a tiny, yellow-bellied bird froze to peer at the roe with bright, curious eyes. The bird was a tam tit, or willow warbler. His mate touched down beside him as the doe passed by, and together they flew to their nest in a fern clump, carrying green caterpillars.

Voles scurried through the grass where yellow pimpernels trailed slender stems. The doe stopped when a cushat swung low across her path, to alight on a low branch with a clatter of white-barred wings; she had a nest in the birch, to which she was returning to lay her second egg. The doe continued when the bird settled on her wafer nest, and presently reached the end of the thicket, where crawling mists were thinning in the morning sun.

Three hundred yards ahead was Cowther Wood, with Cowther Farm at its northern end, among the elms and sycamores across the road. In Cowther Farm were the only white owls for many miles, the ghostly Screecher and his mate, who lived in the ancient cobwebby doo-cot, where they had five downy owlets on piled-up rat bones between mouldy rafters. At the other end of the wood was a low-lying meadow, or haugh, a green bowl with scattered trees and thickets of gorse, which was a grazing place for the Cowther cattle. From the haugh rose the long ridge of heather and pines where the nightjars nested.

The doe lay down among green fern fronds to chew cud,

while the last of the ground mist trailed away in strands of spun silk. Reed buntings and moss cheepers flew past, twittering and tweeping as they carried grubs to their chicks. A cushat, with breast rosy-tinted in the sun, heeled into the birches on whistling wings; when his wing clatter ceased the doe heard him croodling to his mate, who was at that moment standing on her nest with hunched shoulders laying her second egg. He fell silent when the sudden scolding of small birds brought the doe to her feet, with ears up and nostrils sifting.

Across the open common, flying low and fast from the direction of the haugh, came a dark bird with long tail and rounded wings, with a score of small birds chivying him from behind. The dark bird was Kiki, the sparrow-hawk, who had a nest in a tall larch on the ridge-end slope. Each time he crossed the common he picked up an escort of small birds, any one of which he could have slain in the blink of an eye; but, for reasons known only to himself, he preferred hunting farther afield, killing but rarely in the flock that mobbed him.

Kiki flapped into a tree beside the doe, and shuffled his wings till they were neatly scissored over his tail. He saw her at once, but gave her no more than a glare from his savage, yellow eyes. Everything about Kiki was sharp and keen and needling—from his thin yellow legs and razor-edged talons to his flat, rakish head and fish-hook beak. He was furious at the small birds—tits, buntings, warblers and finches—gossiping round his ear. His piercing eyes, hard and glittering like glass, slew them over and over again. Had they lingered overlong he would have snatched one eventually; but, presently, they began to remember other business, and flew away in twos and threes. Kiki, watching them with unwinking eyes, rubbed an ear against a wing elbow, then stretched himself to the full length of his legs. When he flashed into the birches, hooking round trees as nimbly as a swallow and skimming low over the heather, the doe turned to retrace her steps. Both cushats sat unmoving till Kiki, their arch-enemy, was far away. They had wanted to break out in a frenzy of wings, but were scared to move with the hawk so near. The doe passed below them on her own outgoing trail, keeping to it till she reached the tam tits, still carrying green caterpillars. Turning left to the north fringe, she made haste under the birch cover till she was directly downwind from her fawns. In a thicket of low scrub and tall heather, near a grey, black-ribbed boulder where a pair of wheatears had their nest, she lay down with nose to flank and back to wind.

In the late afternoon, when the birches were a shimmer of green and cushats crooned rhythmically in Cowther, she went to nurse her fawns. The does rose on rubbery legs and came sprawling towards her, buckling at the knees, but the buck, jumping to his feet with a purposeful thrust of slender legs, approached with deliberate, jerky steps. His greedy lips were first to find her teats, starting a flow of milk before the does got a mouth-hold. And, because he was the strongest sucker, besides being the most robust fawn, he finished first to fasten on the doe's fourth nipple.

The doe stood with head erect, wagging her ears against the flies. Three fawns nursing at once, and all boring for headroom, meant much jostling at her hind legs; but she was gentle and patient, uttering low cries of encouragement deep in her throat and never once stamping with a foot. Every now and again she looked over her shoulder to gaze on them with admiration. They nursed two on one side and one on the other. The does had to share the near side for the bouncing buck, appropriating a side to himself, held it stubbornly against them. When the doe was satisfied that they had had enough, she stepped away without haste or roughness, and wheeled quickly to face them.

They stood three abreast, with milk smears showing pale blue against black, shining muzzles, frail, elfin things, with glowing violet eyes and slender legs of sheened silk. They watched her intently but made no attempt to run to her; instead they touched noses, found the milk taste again, and licked each other clean.

Except in size, all three were exactly alike, with muzzles of jet, two white splashes on the upper lip, and white chins edged with black. They had brown wavy coats, a patch of darker brown on hips and rows of white spots on flanks. The dappling on their backs was like a line of snowflakes, but the spots on necks were paler. Their tiny hooves, black and polished, were coloured pale horn at the tips, and each had a white patch, or flag, of dense, soft, cotton wool fur round its invisible tail. Their limpid eyes, with long, sweeping lashes, were innocent of high light.

Tired legs soon forced the doe fawns to flop down in their tracks, but the buck was made of sterner stuff. He kicked and capered like a spring lamb, till he kicked himself right off his feet and went down in a fankle of legs. Rising again, after much struggling on his knees, he danced sideways towards this mother with head askew—splay-legged, bucking, rearing and high-kicking with hooves together. He stumbled, righted himself, back-tracked with chin on chest, then bounced daringly into the air to a height of twelve inches or more. When he fell a second time, the doe decided it was time for them to rest.

Somehow they understood her voiceless command, for they obeyed at once without question or caper. Bounce, the dandiprat dancer, lay where he had fallen, between two woody stems of heather with scraggy flower heads;

but his sisters, struggling to their feet, returned to their former beds. The doe nosed each in turn, and inhaled deeply of the air, before disappearing among the birches. But she went no farther than her lie by the wheatears' stone.

Soon afterwards, the doe fawns fell asleep. The sun, slanting to the west, cast hard shadows and harsh high lights that hid them completely. Bounce lay awake a little longer, with wide eyes roving but every muscle still. Only once did he move, when he curled his milky tongue over his black muzzle, sighing audibly after a momentary heaving of his dappled flanks. He saw a pink-footed woodmouse whisking about the clearing, tits in the trees, and small bees, with sparkling wings, buzzing among the yellow flowers on the bank. But he saw it all without betraying movement. And, presently, his eyes closed too in sleep.

He woke when Screecher, the ghost owl from Cowther, flew overhead on downy wings at sunset. But it was not the white, silent bird that had disturbed his slumber.

Faintly, to his baby ears, came a rustling and scuffing, then the *pat-pat-pat* of fearless feet on firm ground. As the patter of feet came nearer, his nostrils closed on the faint odour of musk, then dilated for full reception before wrinkling in distaste. In a moment he saw a low-set, sinuous beast, tawny in the red glow of the sunset, weaving and darting with belly to earth, where the woodmouse had scurried a few hours before. It had scurried there again while the fawn slept, journeying to and fro with nesting material, and now the stoat was sorting out the maze of trails.

At that moment Bounce knew fear, and shuddered involuntarily. But stronger than his urge to panic was the age-old instinct that bound him to silence and absolute movelessness in face of peril. So he lay still, with his fear

25

showing only in his eyes. And across the clearing, guided by the same inherited wisdom, his sisters also lay still, with the same fear in their eyes and the same scent in their nostrils.

As it happened, the stoat had no idea that three fawns lay close to his trail. At that moment he was interested in the wood-mouse, for he was wild with hunger, and this was the first fresh line he had found since leaving his den in a rabbit burrow beyond Cowther. His movements were quick and nervous, snake-like in dart and recoil, and his rippling, feathering run had the mark of all the weasels. The woodmouse was doomed if he stuck to its line, for few indeed were those who escaped when he once put his nose to a trail. But, suddenly, he stopped weaving, to turn with a quick paw movement in the direction of the watching Bounce.

And it happened, as it sometimes does happen when pure chance leads a hunting beast to unsuspected prey. The stoat raced up to, and on to, the crouching fawn, unaware until the actual moment of contact that any living thing lay in this path; for the fawn of the roe, like the leveret of the hare, or the brooding partridge on her nest, seems to lack betraying body scent in the first days of its helplessness.

The stoat's first reaction was one of alarm. He cringed back, tissing and chipping, then launched the overpowering attack of musk which was his inevitable response to sudden fear. But the truth came to him almost in the same instant, and he returned with the speed of a striking viper.

Deer kids were out of his line. Though he had seen many of them running with their dams, this was the first he had ever found weak and unattended. But if they were out of his line, they were not beyond his will. Vindictive and savage, he was prepared to tackle anything he could catch and hold. Size meant nothing to him in the urgency of his lust to kill. The victim lying at his feet, warm and quivering, was helpless to resist, incapable of fighting back; so he struck, and buried his needle teeth deep in the skin of Bounce's neck.

The sudden, sharp stab of pain brought a wild cry from the fawn. Half bleat, half bellow, it was a cry of despair and an appeal for succour. Thus early in life Bounce learned the anguish of physical pain. The instinct that bade him lie silent and still as a safeguard against prowling foes was instantly forgotten in the reality of active peril. So he wailed for his mother and kicked, and struggled to his feet, trying to shake the horror from his bleeding neck, for he was not like the stoated rabbit which is prepared to surrender its life without a fight. And all the while his sisters crouched mute and wide-eyed and motionless.

In her thicket, the doe heard the fawn's first cry. She crashed from her cover in one tremendous leap, with fear and anger flaming in her heart. Spurning caution and question she bounded at full speed through the birches, and both stoat and fawn heard the noise of her coming. Before the marauder's palate had time to thrill to the first trickle of blood she was at the clearing, full of the reckless courage of outraged motherhood.

If the stoat had been wise, he would have rushed for the nearest tree or flashed into the nearest hole the instant he lost his grip on the fawn, instead of waiting for the doe. But he was half-crazed with the excitement of slaughter, blooded to the point of recklessness, and probably ignorant of the fury that can fire the roe.

When the doe burst into the clearing he coiled back like a compressed spring, hissing with uncovered teeth. But this demonstration of fury was lost on the deer. Sidestepping Bounce, who had wobbled forward to meet her,

27

she struck out viciously with a forefoot. In that fatal moment the stoat's sanity returned, and he tried to twist away. Too late! Her hoof struck him full on the chest, sending him kicking half way towards the crouching does. With murder in her heart, the doe followed him up, rearing and striking, while the doe fawns jumped from their lies and Bounce hustled her from behind.

The stoat spat and nickered and chattered, but he was unable to elude her because his front was stove in. Again the doe struck out with a foot, and this time her blow was deadly. It caught the stoat fairly on the back, breaking his fragile spine. Blood spurted from the wound, for the blow was solid and the doe's hoof had an edge like a knife. The body jumped and twisted and curled and rolled across the clearing, a thing of corded muscle and fantastic energy. The doe pursued the dead-living thing, pounding it again and again, with a savagery her gentle heart had never known.

And, when she at last turned to her fawns, satisfied with her vengeance, the stoat resembled nothing that had ever roamed the woods.

3

THE DOE WAS NOT STAMPEDED INTO MOVING HER
family from the Heatherfield birches. Her fawn was
none the worse for his terrifying experience, serious
though it might have been; and stoats were not among
those she feared. The discovery, and attack, had been the
rarest kind of accident. But her faith in the horseshoe
clearing was shaken, so she led her fawns at daybreak to
the thickest cover of Heatherfield.

At first, Bounce was afraid to be left alone, protesting
vigorously and rising to follow his mother each time she
nudged him to his couch. But he was too young to follow
at foot. And the law of the wild laid it down that he
should lie where his mother left him, quiet and unmoving,
until her return. So the doe was inexorable, and kept pushing him down—gently and persuasively, because she understood the terror in his baby heart; yet firmly, because
she knew that obedience to rule was the price of survival.

And Bounce yielded in the end, as much from milk-
drowsiness and tired legs as from any sense of discipline.
His rebellion was prompted solely by fear, of the kind that
can overcome ancestral wisdom. Conscious of no treason
of nature, he knew only that he had been afraid, and that
his mother had answered his cry of distress. It did not
occur to him to rebel because sticking to the rules had
already failed to save him; all he knew was that he
didn't want his mother to leave him again. Yet he let her
go at last, and slept. And the pattern of his life was
restored. So, when he awoke in the bright morning, to find

her still absent, he uttered no cry of protest that might be heard by dangerous ears.

From that day, however, his waking hours were spent watching and listening for his mother returning. He was always first to rise and run to her, first to nurse, last to settle when she was ready to leave. At first, she left them for long periods, coming to them only when they needed her milk. At dusk and daybreak, when she went out to graze, they had to lie patiently until her return. But, as day followed day of bright skies and warm sunshine, and their quiet was not disturbed, she began to spend more and more time with them. She waited, after nursing them, while they butted and capered, withdrawing only when they sought their separate forms to rest tired legs. And, in the night, she lay down close by them between her spells of grazing and browsing.

When they were a week old, and strong on their legs, they spent much time in capers, which made for resilient muscles and increasing stamina. It was then the doe allowed them to follow her out at her evening and morning feeds, and to lie up with her during the day in her thick harbour of heather and purple grass. But, if she were alarmed, as when she heard gunfire in Cowther or a dog barking on the common, the old order was restored; then they had to crouch, quiet and invisible as woodlice, till she returned from her quest.

The fawns' first morning in the open was one of sky haze and lark song, with a puff of wind ruffling the birches. While the doe grazed through bog cotton and moor grass, they bounced about, kicking their heels in wild delight. That morning Bounce was boisterous, the wound on his neck a mere knot of skin, the stoat and the musk nausea no more than a memory.

Before many minutes had passed he discovered an exciting game. Drawing away from his sisters for perhaps ten yards, he turned, pranced, came back at speed, stopped, and kicked high and sideways with his hindfeet together. Liking the game, he repeated the performance, while the little does tried to copy him. Then he tried to leap clear over one of his sisters, but failed in the attempt after striking her with a hoof. So he decided he didn't like the idea and joined them in a three-headed butting match instead.

They played without thought of danger or concealment; the doe was present, and such thoughts were for her. Every now and again she glanced up from her grazing to watch their pranks, then resumed with a shake of her head. Twice they ran to her, to nurse with much butting and furrowing of earth with feet. And twice she stood patiently for them, with head high and ears tuned to the air. Standing still, or grazing, her senses were ever alert for any threat to her fawns.

Bounce wandered away after the second suckling, to explore the world up to twenty yards from his mother. He found it a bewildering world, full of sound and movement.

At the big grey boulder, its black ribs glistening and its moss stars sparkling with dew, he met a bird coloured exactly like it, with grey body, dark wing edges, and a black eye-stripe. It was the cock wheatear, carrying a beakful of caterpillars. The wheatear said *chak-chak*, and flirted his tail, then disappeared into a dark hole under a stone. He had five chicks there, which he had to care for himself, for his mate had been eaten by Kiki, the sparrow-hawk, two days before.

The wheatear flew to a dead tree, with ragged bark, only three roe-bounds away, returning to the boulder with more caterpillars before Bounce had blinked twelve times. He had to work very hard to feed his fledgling family. In one hour, the previous day, he had made ninety-six visits to the nest with flies and grubs.

Bounce moved on when the wheatear flew out again to his tree, inching forward uncertainly till he came to a rush-grown ditch, with sky-blue stars of brooklime spangling every opening. A reed bunting, or coal head, flew from a tall rush clump where it had a nest, startling him momentarily but frightening him not at all. Then he noticed a fat little beast, with brown coat and short tail, sitting on the thatch. He liked the look of this fat little beast with the beaver face, so he reached out to smell it. At that moment Kiki flashed low overhead on his morning patrol, heralded by the *shuggying* of a magpie in the birches. The vole vanished at once among rush stems and Bounce fled back to his mother.

She had her head up before he arrived, looking in the opposite direction, for she was more concerned about the magpie's salute to Kiki than she was with her fawn's stage fright. With ears cupped forward, she stood staring straight ahead, an exquisite creature, with flanks full and round again, and the old bloom on her skin. Seeing Kiki, she knew the magpie hadn't lied. The long-tailed bird dipped out sideways from the birches, spread his wings, and swept away in rising flight towards Cowther. He had just eaten the cushat's eggs.

Bounce left on another foray as the pigeons came out to circle above their despoiled nest, while the doe, reassured by the promptings of her nose, returned to her grazing. She always paid attention to the *shu-shu-shuggy* of magpies, recognising them as the most alert watchdogs in the woods.

The sun's rim topped the mist banks and the morning was suddenly warm. Swifts from Cowther Farm passed overhead on long, curved wings, black crescents against the sky. Above the common peewits plunged and looped on woolly wings, their white fronts flashing in the sun's level rays. Bounce halted beside a jungle of meadowsweet to rub eye on knee, then stayed to smell the opening flower clusters, reaching up to them with neck at full stretch. But he found the poison-fragrance distasteful and danced away to rejoin his mother.

The deer filed slowly into the birches to lie up for the day, stepping to one side on the fringe to avoid a hen pheasant with seven chicks whisking at her heels. Ahead lay the horseshoe clearing, but the doe sheered away from it deliberately, as she had done since her bloody victory over the stoat. For her, the days of the clearing were over.

Musk taint on the air at dusk made her uneasy, for the smell was fox and she feared for her fawns. At nightfall, with the air clean again and the moon rising pale in a clear sky, she went out to feed alone, leaving the family down till she checked the wood. They were still tiny enough to tempt any big fox with a determined mind, so she wanted them all in one place, out of sight, instead of distracting her on her quest, or stravaiging where one could be cut off and chopped before she could intervene.

Finding no sign of fox in the wood, she went out to graze, with her uneasiness almost gone. She cropped grass hastily while the moon silvered in the darkening blue of the sky. She could hear the eldritch shrieking of Screecher as he hunted the Cowther stackyard for rats, and the bubble and hoot of a tawny owl beyond the ridge. Normal threads of sound in the fabric of the night they had, for her, no special significance. Then a big hare crashed through the rushes behind her, in a wild run that electrified her on the instant. The hare had come from the wood; and anything fit to send out a hare in panic was big enough to menace her fawns.

Without chewing on the last rip of grass, she bounded for the wood, and was beside her fawns before the hare had crossed the common. All three were lying quietly—snug, safe and at ease; there were no dangerous scents on

33

the wind. Yet the doe was far from satisfied. The hare's wild run was not explained. Then she saw, downwind, a fleeting shadow skulking across a neck of moonlight—a fox casting for tidings of deer while he kept his own scent out of the doe's nostrils. He knew there were kids in the thicket; but he didn't know where, and was hoping for betraying movement.

All the doe's uneasiness returned. She trembled with mounting anger. With a sudden, bold leap she dashed out to meet the prowler. But the fox, who had five cubs and a crippled vixen in a whinstone quarry two miles away, knew just what a deer could do with its feet, and didn't wait for her to come up. Conceding the point at once, he streaked through the moon-silvered birches, content to have his skin intact but determined to try again. The doe harried him far across the common, without making contact with her feet. When she returned to her fawns she was no less nervous than before; she had driven off a fox, but she knew he would be back.

And he did come back, early the following morning, with the wind on his face and murder in his heart. Again the doe saw him skulking about downwind, with his fine brush gathering the dew, and lips curled in a sly grin. A scouting magpie, spying him from the air, pitched above his head to shower down abuse and birch leaves, while it danced on its perch with neck feathers on end. The doe lent her ears to the bird, but kept her eyes on the fox till he sat down to ponder. While he pondered she tapped the earth nervously with a forehoof; when he rose, with brush slack and tongue hanging from the side of his mouth, she leaped to the assault. And the fox bolted as before.

The magpie, flying ahead of the fox, yattered hysterically as he swung away from the trees, but his altered accent was lost on the doe. At that moment she saw only the fox, and her selective ears missed the bird's change of meaning. She was on the enemy's heels when he reached the thinning trees, ready to lash out with her feet if he turned or hesitated when suddenly two men appeared, close up, straight ahead, both carrying shotguns. The fox swerved into deep heather as a gun went up; the doe checked and took a great leap sideways; the magpie's warning voice was tossed back on the wind. The shotgun roared as the deer turned, and the pigeons went up in Cowther.

The choked charge of No. 4 shot ripped heather in the wake of the fox, but he snaked on, belly to earth, unhit and hoping for miracles. Two barrels belched death in duet, a right from the second gun and a left from the first. The fox was rolling over with his tongue gathering peat when the doe felt the hot impact of shot on her hip. The shock staggered her round broadside, for the range was eighteen yards. A second shot from the same gun struck her behind the left shoulder, clean through to the heart. She took two curving bounds, threw up her head, buckled at the knees, and rolled over on her side, close to the fox who was gripping tongue between teeth in death. For a moment she lay with two legs in the air, rigid and shaking; then they relaxed, and dropped, till she was stretched out forehoof to forehoof and hind to hind.

Blood, the colour of rowanberries in autumn, was oozing from her closed mouth and welling on to her white chin when the men ran to her with exultant shouts. Blue gunsmoke hung like a fine, transparent cloud among the birch foliage till it was dispersed by the morning wind. The men dropped guns and bent to examine the deer.

"Well, ye've gotten your deer, and a fox tae, in a wanner," said the man who had shot the fox. "The deer must've riz it in the wid."

"Uh-huh! But I'd rather had the buck I lost in Glencryan. This'll be useless for meat, but the skin looks no' too bad at that. Will you bleed it, and I'll collect the fox?"

The moocher pulled out a tobacco knife with an edge like a razor, and did the gralloch with quick, expert hands. He had no feelings, one way or the other, about the doe, being a practical man, poacher and rabbit catcher, who killed to sell or for payment from an employer. The morning's work with the shooting tenant meant beer money for the evening, and meat for his dogs.

The shooting tenant's attitude to living things was different. He belonged to that peculiar fraternity whose interest in living things is confined to what can be seen along the barrels of a gun. He shot hawks for killing song birds, weasels for killing rabbits, and anything at all, except singing birds, because he had to have a target for his gun. When he wanted to shoot a deer, he shot one. The fact that the deer might be suckling young had no bearing on the matter at all. It was the moocher who felt the jag of conscience.

"This beast's being sookit," he said. "There'll be kids aboot somewhere."

"They'll be all right," replied the other, "and we'd never find them anyway. Young deer have protective colouring, you know, and they're ill tae find. That's how they manage tae survive among sae many damn' foxes! And they're hardy enough. They'll manage. Deer don't die that easy."

"Well—A doot it. The auld yin's fair fu' o' milk. It must be but mornin' wi' them yet."

The shooting tenant reloaded his gun. "There's nothing we can do . . ." he said.

"That'll be right. Well, we'd best get this load tae the caur. A'll lug the deer. You tak the fox."

As they left, the shooting tenant spoke: "By the bye, Pate. I . . . ah . . . well, there's no point in saying anything aboot this tae anybody. I mean . . ."

But he didn't say what he meant.

4

SCREECHER, THE WHITE OWL, FLYING OVER THE COMMON in the windless dusk, heard a strange cry among the birches and wafted down to discover the cause. The nightjar, hawking above the trees in swallow flight silent as the owl's, checked and swerved in flight when the ghost bird crossed his path, then glided away without lingering to hearken. A brown hare, returning to her leverets in their forms among cotton grass, halted with ears erect in question, and a home-going cattleman on the road near Cowther Farm slowed pace to listen.

The owl, with long, white legs outstretched, clutched for a foothold on a slim birch twig that bent with his weight. Folding his downy wings, after much wild flapping to keep his balance, he craned forward to stare wide-eyed into the thicket. A weasel, mousing in the depths of grass, stopped mousing when he heard wings among the birch leaves and was missed by the dark eyes of the owl. While the weasel crouched mute in a vole creep Screecher searched the ground, swaying on his perch with head thrust out below the level of his feet. And in a moment he discovered the fawns—all three; with Bounce between him and the hidden weasel.

Bounce was standing half crouched in the ground gloom, with hind legs splayed out backwards, when the owl pitched in the tree. He froze and fell silent before Screecher had folded his wings, instinct reasserting control in the face of visual peril. Screecher screamed a rasping scream, like a file on the teeth of a saw, and lifted

37

away, tearing off twin birch leaves gathered under a wing. The man on the road, seeing him crossing towards Cowther, resumed his journey, convinced he had been listening to some vocal display of the owl.

Bounce scraped the earth with a forehoof when the owl had gone—his normal action when preparing his bed. But his scraping was mechanical. He wasn't tired and had no thought of lying down. His mind was concerned entirely with his fear and loneliness; his eyes, ears and nose alert for the first sign of his mother. The scraping was prompted by instinct, to restore the pattern he had disrupted by moving and breaking silence. When the owl appeared, he should have been couched and silent; instead, he had been on his feet, calling. His self-advertisement had brought discovery, and might yet bring real peril. It had also brought fear—fear of the unknown—though it had come in the shape of a harmless owl. So guardian instinct was driving him to restore the pattern.

But of such things Bounce knew nothing; nor could he know. While he scraped with a hoof, and directed his ears to capture every sound of the night, his sisters watched intently. Throughout the owl's visit they had remained mute and motionless. More placid in temperament, they had not yet voiced their plaint of hunger and loneliness. Their spotted flanks heaved gently in rhythm with their breathing, which was movement they could not control. But Bounce, perhaps because the sum of his experience had been greater, was fretful, ill at ease, and on the point of panic.

For some minutes after the owl had gone he remained quiet, with nostrils dilated, and ears constantly changing their angle of question. A breath of wind started the leaves whispering without distracting his ears. They were already too highly selective to mistake leaf talk. Then a rustle that was not of the wind jerked both ears forward. The fawn tensed, with knees bent and rump down, ready for a wild, high-angle bound to safety at the first hint of danger.

Pat-pat-pat! The sound was feet in grass—tiny feet, quickly moving feet, the feet of one who had nought to fear. Bounce put frightened questions to the wind and, suddenly, his nostrils found a smell he knew, a smell he would never forget, a smell that brought stark terror to his baby heart—the musk taint of a questing weasel.

Pat-pat-pat! The weasel was weaving in circles seeking for mouse smell. He was in vile temper because his hunting had been interrupted by the owl. With his bright eyes peering through the twin leaders of a birch seedling he sat up for the space of two heartbeats in the listening attitude beloved by his kind. Bounce tightened for a leap when the slim, sinuous body snaked across the ground, and broke screaming from his hiding place when the tiny hunter turned in his direction.

His noisy take-off started the weasel, making him draw back like a viper after striking. He showed teeth and tissed his displeasure at the further disturbance to his hunting. But he had no designs on the fawns. Passing close to the crouching does, he snarled without noise and showed them the colour of his teeth, because it was his nature to snarl and display teeth to every living thing he disliked or feared. He listened to the noise of Bounce's retreat, scratched ribs with a hindfoot, then, finding a mouse trail, became engrossed at once in his own affairs.

Out on the open heather, halfway to the road, Bounce came to a halt, trembling, with lips open and nostrils wide. Holding his head high, he checked every direction with his ears and the wind's breath with his nose, standing in the half-crouch so characteristic of the roe in uncertainty.

But tang of heather, birch scent and the smell of moist earth were all his nose could own. To his ears came the skirling of Screecher, the reedy weeping of peewits, and the rhythmic, wooden churring of a nightjar. And again he was overwhelmed by hunger and fear, and a terrible loneliness which won the battle over instinctive silence.

So he cried—plaintively and poignantly; now like a child in distress, now like a wounded hare, his voice rising and falling, proclaiming to the whole countryside that he was a baby in distress. But there were no dangerous ears to note or surmise, so no stealthy footsteps approached. Instead, there was silence; silence of which he was now afraid. The urge to total panic increased with every cry he uttered. Breaking point came when a fat frog touched his tiny forehooves as it clambered over the grass. The touch was like an electric shock to the fawn. Kicking out blindly, he bounded into the air and fled headlong, leaving behind a frog writhing with a broken spine, the victim of a chance stroke of his knife-edged hoof.

When he stopped for the second time he was panting with mouth open, and only twenty yards from the dark pines of Cowther. The serried pine tops were like black teeth against the fading pink and saffron of the western sky. Night was falling. Soon it would settle, dark and brooding, like the feathers of an owl.

Bounce, recovering his breath, stepped forward till he was clear of cotton grass that reached to his chin and tufted rushes that out-topped his ears. He stopped in an open space where a thread of water trickled, sinking in mud to the fetlocks. Suddenly, the headlights of a car stabbed through the gloom of the wood, catching Screecher in the beams as he flew home with a fat vole in his feet. Bounce cringed back, trapping the slim stem of a cuckoo flower in the cleft of a hindhoof, and crouched low, with all four legs stretched and rigid.

The headlights swung in a wide arc as the car turned between the flanking drystane dykes of the Cowther hairpin, sweeping over birch and rowan and heather, fireweed and moor grass, and dazzling the eyes of the fawn. In face of this new terror he screamed and bolted in new panic. But he could no longer make haste. The tall grass and clutching heather had tired his slim legs, and he scrambled his way towards Cowther with the rocking-horse movements of an ambling hare.

A stone's throw from the woodside cart track, close by a straggling briar, his knees folded under him and he fell heavily on his side, spent and exhausted. One of the briar tendrils, thick as his foreleg, raked his side with thorn spikes like the teeth of foxes, but he was too worn out to care. He panted noisily, with mouth open, while the beating of his heart could be seen on his ribs. A rabbit, feeding up to the briar, failed to distract him, though he could smell it and see its white fud. He knew, without telling, that it could do him no harm. With muzzle to flank, and white chin resting on upgathered hind legs, he closed his eyes. He was asleep, shivering slightly, when Screecher flew out on his second foray.

At midnight, the owl skirled on the wood edge and flew into a spreading oak with a field mouse in his claws. He had just clutched it from a bank where it had burrowed into a bumble bee nest for a feast of bee grubs, and wanted it for himself, having already carried in two voles and a young rat to his mate in the farm doo-cot. Bounce, watching him flapping into the oak, showed no fear. When Screecher had settled, he rose weakly, having just enough strength to thrust himself from his knees after much trying.

Screecher saw him stepping on to the rutted cart road

as he was manœuvring his mouse under his feet. The owl grasped his prey by the head, to stretch it against the pull of his feet. Then he started to swallow it whole, bowing, shaking his head, grimacing and bulging his throat as if the effort was choking him. With the mouse tail still sticking from his beak he paused to glare when the fawn stumbled in a wheel rut. Then he scratched his right ear where fleas were tickling. When Bounce rose unsteadily from the wheel rut, he swept from his perch gulping down the rest of his mouse as he flew.

The cart track, unkempt and grass grown, followed the wood edge to the joining road at the far hairpin. It was a rough road of whinstones, pressed into the earth by the wheels of carts, double rutted from wood-end to farthest pasture. Along the woodside only grass and bracken grew, but the growth on the opposite verge, clear of the life-stealing gloom of the pines, was profuse. Bounce held nervously away from the wood as he walked slowly towards the farm. He was lost, completely lost, and cold, and perilously near the sleep that lasts for ever.

When he reached the hairpin verge, pinched, and knock-kneed and drooping, he wrinkled his nostrils, for the road was newly surfaced and smelt of tar. A black and white cat, returning to kittens in the stable after a hunting foray in the wood, crossed the road in front of him with a small rabbit in her mouth. She fluffed her tail like a bottle brush because she was afraid of the fawn, and Bounce bolted along the newly tarred road because he was afraid of the cat. Thus, fear brings fleeting strength to over-taxed muscles and nerves.

When the cat reached her blind, mewing kittens squirming in their hay nest in a manger, Bounce was fifty yards up the road, standing with trembling legs under an ancient ash whose branches and roots reached to the opposite verge. The drystane dyke between him and the ash trunk was two and a half times his height, yet, for some reason, he suddenly wanted to get over, and was prepared to try.

At the first attempt he fell back heavily, scraping his soft muzzle on the tarred road when he rolled on his side with legs sprawling. At the second attempt his forehooves scraped green moss from the dyke face, and he fell, winded, again. Rising, he rushed at the dyke in a kind of fury, knocking himself about and falling repeatedly. Failing at that point, he started running up and down in a frenzy—the dyke had become the focal point of all his fears, something to be overcome at any cost. He was in a panic born of fear, loneliness, hunger and frustration. He saw himself trapped, with the dyke the barrier to freedom. So he threw himself at it, recklessly, till he had blood on his white underlip, moss on muzzle and shoulder, and grit in the clefts of his hooves. Then, when he was ready to drop—when it seemed as if his heart must burst—he found a point where stones had been removed, reducing the height at the gap by half. His next rush took him up and through, and he fell with falling pebbles into the kitchen garden of Cowther Farm.

Tall grass and cow parsnips on the other side, crowding close on thick bushes of currant and gooseberry, afforded the right kind of cover to soothe his jangled nerves, and he squirmed into hiding licking his lips. He wanted to cry out at once, but had breath enough only to moan and whimper. Yet, blown though he was, and almost past heeding, his ears still heard the subdued *kwer-r-k* and throaty chuckle under the next bush, where a white hen was sitting on fifteen eggs. She was angry, but not alarmed, at the intrusion on her privacy. Earlier in the night she had been afraid as well as angry when a prowling hedgehog put her off for twenty minutes, while he tried his teeth on every egg without success. Unable to span them

with his teeth, he couldn't break them, so he left in search
of slugs while the hen returned to her secret treasures.

Each time Bounce moved his head the hen said *kwer-r-k*
and ruffled her feathers. Unable to see him, she was
simply demonstrating at his presence. But Bounce,
watching her with an ear, was content to ignore her and
get his breath back. When he got it back he called out
at once.

For ten seconds he wailed and cried, betraying his state
and whereabouts to ears far beyond Cowther. His wailing
carried as far as the bleat of a Blackface lamb across a
Highland glen. The white hen *kwerked* again, with all her
feathers raised. Bounce stopped to listen. And, before he
had taken ten more breaths, his plaint was answered.

Waugh-waugh-waugh! Yap-yap-yap! The farm collie, and
terrier, had heard, and awaited his reply. Bounce could
hear the rattle of their nails against the door of the barn
where they slept on a hollowed bale of straw. The dogs
barked again, scraped at the barn door, and whined
excitedly. The big Leghorn rooster, sitting on a rafter in
the cartshed with favourite hens, stretched his neck and
crowed. He was answered by the beefy grey cock that
roosted in a big chestnut tree beside the miller's cottage in
the glen, across the burn. Then three cockerels crowed at
the farm four fields away. Their calls were faint, but were
heard by the Cowther Leghorn, who challenged louder
than before.

Bounce bleated again, starting the dogs for the third
time. The cat in the manger stopped licking nipples to
listen. Screecher's mate, heaving and swaying as she
covered restless owlets, blinked once with a lustrous eye
and excluded the disturbance from her hearing list. On
the other side of the wall slept Cairns of Cowther, his
wife and two budgerigars in cages. Cairns awoke at
Bounce's second cry, scratching a hairy arm.

44

"A hare in a snare, soonds like. Or mebbe cooch by a wheezel." His wife wasn't listening, so he turned over and went to sleep. He had the same facility as the owl for being deaf to what he didn't want to hear.

The dogs stood prick-eared behind the door waiting for Bounce: but Bounce didn't call. Instead, he fell asleep. And the owl slept, and the cat, and the Leghorn on his rafter. The fawn whimpered in sleep, wagging his ears, and sucked dream nipples in deep content. And the night held no more terrors.

Cock-crow at peep of day came muffled from the cart-shed rafters. Bounce opened his eyes, and shivered on his bed, for the morning was chill, with a heavy dew. Stars still winked faintly in the dark sky overhead, but there was a brightness in the east where gulls were flying. Birds, seeing the light, sang in the gloaming—tam tit and robin, dunnock, shilfa and mavis. The dawn throng's chorus swelled as the light spread, and a wood owl hooted in Cowther. Screecher flew into the doo-cot and did not come out again.

Bounce rose, struggling shakily from his knees, when he could see the eyes of the white hen on her nest, and arched his back with legs at full stretch. When he tried to scratch an ear with a hindfoot he fell on his side; so he rose and rubbed it against his shoulder instead. It was itching with dew.

He left the garden by the open gate, where dock and nettles grew thick. The black and white cat, sitting round-eyed at a mousehole in the cartshed gable, arched her back when he passed, then turned again to her vigil. Bounce walked with slow steps till the dogs barked, when he bolted with old fear born anew. Hens were already scratching in the dung midden, from which steam was rising, and rats were starting to play follow-my-leader along the wall top because they knew that Screecher was abed. From the midden the tarred road dropped steeply between stately elms to the burn, with Cowther wood on the left and a field of young corn on the right.

The gate into the cornfield was two russet larch poles, slung between elms and tied with string. The elms were ringed where wire had bitten. Bounce walked under the larch poles without stooping, pricked his ears and sniffed with tongue showing between his lips. Against the deep green of the corn he stood out as clearly as a red fox on a lawn. A magpie, dipping from Cowther towards the farm midden, saw him at once, and said so. The fawn cowered, spreading his white flag to the size of a first elm leaf, while the magpie, flicking his wings and scissoring his green spear tail, flew into a tree for a closer look.

The magpie said *chuck-uck* in his most provocative accent. Bounce retreated under the ample skirts of a big elm with head down, legs rigid and flag still spread, betraying his alarm. Getting no response, the bird started to shuffle along his perch, chuckling in his throat. When he had sent down six elm leaves and a twig as thick as his leg, he flew away suddenly, yattering in urgent alarm. Bounce watched him skimming low over the garden dyke, without understanding that his sudden departure was due to the appearance of a man and a dog on the cornfield headrig.

But he did sense danger when he saw and smelt them, and went down on his knees as the terrier, racing ahead of the man, started chasing rabbits in the corn. When ten Khaki Campbell ducks rose to fly, the man called off the dog. Nine flew quacking, rising to tree height; the tenth flew with wings brushing the green corn blades, uttering only muffled sounds because it had in its bill a chaffinch it had just caught in the field. Bounce was flat on the ground when the terrier, yelping and leaping, curved away to run back to its master.

Man and dog disappeared into the glen, sending the pigeons up from the oaks on the slope. Bounce rose and crossed the cornfield, getting an unafraid glance from a leveret that had lain there since the terrier's run-through. On the cornfield edge he hesitated before crossing the track of man and dog under the oaks. Stepping forward after a brief survey by ears and nose, he was immediately chin deep in tall grass, stitchwort and red campion with petals cleft like his hooves. Tam tits with bright eyes, and wrens with erect tails, pitched on dead branch and tree stump to watch as he went down the slope with the gait and appearance of a hare. The ground cover was thick under the trees and Bounce was hidden by bracken and foxgloves and brushwood tangles till he reached the levels.

Across the burn was the miller's cottage, its white-washed walls concealed by century-old yews and high-reaching rhododendrons. Bounce turned right through drifts of bluebells, skirted a patch of butterbur, or bad man's rhubarb, with leaves like the ears of elephants, and reached the burn bank under twisted alders. Here were blue stars of speedwell, which he reached down to nibble, and pink-white, slender flower heads of enchanter's nightshade, sown by sheep which had gathered spiny fruits in their fleeces from parent plants in Heatherfield.

On the shingle, flashing talons of water snatched at his hooves, so he swung away, pivoting on his hindfeet, to continue his quest along the bank. The faint calling of a man, and the far barking of a dog, froze him under a leaning alder, beside a quiet backwater where a cushat was swimming with slow, flapping movements of its wings. When the pigeon had made two circuits of the foam-girded pool he left without haste but with one ear harking back. He could not know that one of his sisters had just been chopped and broken up on Heatherfield by a fast, hard-mouthed, smoke-coloured lurcher, owned by the man who had slit the doe's belly with his tobacco knife.

Travelling for a mile upstream, hidden for most of the way by dense growth of reeds and wild liquorice and hemlock, he emerged under a sheer rock face, crowned with green spreads of woodrush, and dripping water over black, mossed ledges. In a grass tussock, beside a lichened stump, a robin was feeding grey wagtail chicks which it had forcibly adopted after a brown rat had killed its own chicks in their nest on the lip of the burn. Four days had passed but the parent wagtails were still flying about with food, and Bounce could hear them calling in the alders as he squeezed along the water's edge under the dripping rock.

Beyond the rock the ground was level and marshy. Bounce crossed the first neck of squelching ground with mud blistering between the clefts of his hooves. Ahead of him the ground rose gradually to a drier half acre—a kind of plateau of rough, bleached grass where fox cubs, recently killed after being caught by paws in gins, had played in the weeks before he was born. Rushes and meadowsweet claimed the lower levels. At the northwest end, in a deeper hollow, was a leafed-up waterhole, hidden by osiers, and willow, and hawthorn. The ground rose steeply on the south side, concealing the foxes' playground completely from road and farms only a minute's crow flight away.

Bounce breasted the rise among knee-high thorns, and reached the flat top without quickening breath. And, suddenly, he was on the alert, with head high and ears forward.

Twenty-five yards away he saw the image of his mother —a sleek roe doe with nose to grass while she scratched her ear with a hindfoot. Nearby were her twin dappled fawns, capering in circles, prancing forward to touch head to head, with forelegs splayed, then dancing backwards kicking their heels. Bounce stared fixedly at the doe till she stopped scratching her ear and tossed her head; then he turned to gaze at the fawns. They were dappled like himself and about the same age and height. When they pranced towards each other again, rearing, and jumping sideways with heads askew, he turned his own head quickly in half-hearted imitation.

Involuntarily, his legs took him forward half a dozen strides towards the playing fawns, but he stopped short when the doe, throwing up her head, wheeled like lightning with muzzle level and ears twitching. Bounce had the wind on his face, so there was no news of him on the air. But the doe had good eyes, trained in that environment, and had seen him moving. Having seen him moving she could now distinguish him, in spite of the colour mimicry that matched him against his background of browns and greens and broken sunlight. And, having picked him out, she held him with her eyes while she minced round the wind to try and get him in her nose.

But, suddenly, as if satisfied by the evidence of her eyes, she stopped, and turned to her fawns. They came skipping towards her at once, as if recalled by some subtle signal. She nosed each in turn, then turned her gaze back to Bounce. The fawns thrust muzzles under her flank, forcing up one hindleg, then another, as they dunted her udder; but she stepped away impatiently, leaving them lip-licking in wonder. She was still interested in the intruding fawn.

Bounce, responding to the fawns' actions, began to lick his lips. Six times in as many seconds his pink tongue appeared from the side of his mouth to curl over his shining muzzle. Then he gave voice to a faint call, rarely heard by human ears.

Eep. Eep. Nee-eep.

The doe strode halfway from her fawns, stopped, lifted her left hindleg, and licked the hair tuft under her hock. She tongued hoof and cannon, tossed her head, and turned back to her family. Her fawns danced towards her and tried to nurse again.

Eep-eep. Eep. Nee-eep.

The fawns heard, too, and pricked their ears. They knew the call because it was their own greeting to the doe when they saw her approaching after an absence. It was also their hunger plaint when she was reluctant to let them nurse. So they pranced towards Bounce, unafraid and eager, heedless of the doe's foot stamping in half-formed disapproval. But they did not come right up to him. They stopped, halfway between him and the doe, shaking their heads, dancing on their hind legs like circus ponies, and jumping in half circles. The doe wagged her ears and ripped a mouthful of grass. When Bounce moved forward to join her fawns she glanced at him once, went down on her knees and settled to chew cud. And her fawns knew she was unconcerned about the intruder.

They were eager to play, after they had touched noses with the newcomer and licked his muzzle. Bounce tried, but stumbled twice because he could not cope with their electric spirits and nourished muscles. He needed milk before he could be happy; strength before he could play. And he knew where there was milk in abundance.

So he approached the doe—slowly; not because he was afraid but because he was weary. The doe, chewing, stared at him with her great, soft eyes, and reached out tentatively to smell him. She rose on to her knees, jumped up, and made low noises in her throat; her sense of motherhood had overcome her suspicion. No man can know what thoughts were born in her mind. Perhaps she thought Bounce was her own; certainly she knew he was of her kind, a baby, helpless, hungry, pinched and unutterably weary. When she turned her flank to him, he needed no guidance, and pushed under her as if he would lift her off her feet. The doe, waving her ears, started chewing when a ripple passed up her gullet.

Bounce's quest was over. . . .

5

PATRICK MACPHERSON, RED-BEARDED AND QUIZZICAL, looked down at the limp, whimpering thing which he had just deposited on the kitchen floor of Fin-me-oot Cottage, wondering if he could fan into fire the tiny spark of life that still remained.

The whimpering foundling was a fawn—a tiny doe— fast losing heat and sick unto death. That morning Patrick had heard of a nursing doe killed on Heatherfield, for the moocher had talked over his beer and news had travelled quickly, as it does where oil lamps burn and communications are slow. Later in the forenoon, Patrick had learned from his sister at Heatherfield the further news that Pate's lurcher had killed a fawn, and that another was running in the heather. Then he had heard its cry, and seen it near the spring on the edge of the common.

So he tried to catch the fawn, but failed, being too old to run it down even in its weakened state. Then he persuaded his sister, who lived in Heatherfield Cottage, to turn one of her milking Saanen goats loose in the heather. But the goat had no notions about mothering the fawn, which had given up all thought of concealment, and was moving about in full view of the cottage—stumbling, falling, panting and crying loudly. Yet, when Patrick's sister tried to approach, it found strength to run from her, and a place to hide until she had gone.

"It's a pair wee beast," she said to Patrick, who was reflecting on ways of taking a fawn. "And that

Tamson wi' his dog! Some bodies need their heids looked!"

"Noo—dinna be sair on Pate, noo!" Patrick admonished her, blinking his eyes like an owl. "If his dog hadna kilt the cratur the foxes wid—an' a while later at that. You canna blame Pate ower much for settin' his dog on't."

But his sister was unrepentant.

"Men are a' alike," she asserted. "They've aye tae be killin' something that's hermin' naebody. An' noo I've tae listen tae this beast dirlin' in my ears like a greetin' bairn!"

"Mebbe so. Mebbe so. But you greetin' 'll no' help the cratur noo! No' that I'm sayin' it wisna an awfu' thing tae dae," he added hurriedly, seeing the fire in her eyes, "but beasts get kilt at times, an' there'll aye be young ones tae pay for't."

Then, suddenly, Patrick had thought of his collie—Nell. Wise, soft of mouth, and gentle when instructed, she was fleet enough to catch a pining fawn.

"But she'll coup it, an' maybe hurt it!" his sister objected.

"Better takin' that risk than let the cratur sterve tae daith or be run aff its legs wi' foxes." And Patrick blinked his eyes to drive home his point.

So Bounce's sister came into Patrick's keeping, run down and held by a wise collie bitch till her master arrived to take over.

And, after much persuading—after she had kicked and struggled and panted and screamed; after she had whimpered and sobbed like a child that has cried itself to exhaustion; after she had refused milk from teats hurriedly borrowed from shepherds—she had at last lipped baby milk from a teaspoon. And, rediscovering hunger, she lost fear, and sucked greedily, spoonful after spoonful, till there was warmth in her blood again and milk all over her muzzle.

In Glencryan Wood, where wind-shaken beeches, giant of frame, shed rain tears on the deep, ground-carpet of their own dead leaves, a six-pointer roebuck, wounded on the neck, was prodding a peeling pine with his antlers.

The buck had trotted through the birch swamp from Braeburn Strip in the rainswept, shaking dawn, getting his red coat darkened and dishevelled in the downpour. The wound on his neck had a commanding itch, but each time he scraped it with a hindfoot he broke the crust without easing the torment, and opened the wound so that it bled anew. Day after day he had scratched it, and always a new crust formed to ensure further annoyance on the morrow.

Besides the annoyance, the wound troubled him in other ways. Unable to turn his head on the wounded side, he could lick neither ribs nor leg nor hoof nor rump. Pain and stiffness made him walk with head high and unmoving; but the greatest scourge of all was the assault of flies. When they crowded on his neck, he could do no more than run and kick and shake his head, or seek heavy shade for doubtful sanctuary.

To the beeches he had made twice-daily visits, at dusk and dawn, following the well-marked deer path from the swamp to his trysting place with the doe who came no more. For two years he had run with her, fighting to win her in the first autumn and fighting again in the second to hold her against all challengers. Each morning he had expected to find her in Glencryan with her new family; each night he had sought her again in vain. The two yearlings, his own family, he had seen more than once. Like him, they kept searching for the mother who had so unaccountably deserted them; but the buck was intolerant of their company and refused to take charge of them.

So the bullet-scarred buck was nearing the point where he would accept the truth. His wound might keep him lingering in Glencryan; but the rutting fire, when it kindled in his blood, would surely drive him out in search of another mate.

6

THE SUNLIGHT LAY ON THE POOL WHERE SPEARS OF
iris glistened. The overhanging trees—sallow and
hawthorn, briar and rambling osier—cast dark shadows
on the surface leaf-pattern, a faded tapestry of bronze and
crimson and gold, on which new colours were shed each
year by the wild gales of November. Flies' wings sang in
the green, cool place; and bees, droning among the yellow
flowers of the sun-sheened flags, revelled in dusty pollen.

Under the osiers, where the sunlight glanced on the
dark, still water, a bird with yellow and scarlet beak sat
on a raised nest of bents the colour of ripe corn. The nest
was built on an exposed osier root and contained seven
cream, spotted eggs on the point of hatching. The brooding
bird had her beak pressed to her breast and her eye on a
fat toad squatting on mud between glossy iris blades.

Across the pool the flag tops swayed, and a second bird
paddled into the sunshine—a waterhen with the same
bright beak as his mate on the nest. He swam across the
pool with jerky movements of his head, his lobed feet
clearing a channel through the deep leaf strata and churning up the mould-dust of many years to swirl in his wake.
Clambering out among straight bur-reeds, he hurried over
creeping roots of osier to his mate on the nest. The mud
was already printed with the tracks of many feet, for this
was the route of both birds to and from their nest.

Beyond the massed iris blades was a thorn thicket
reaching down to the rushes on the margin of the pool. In
the darkest thorn a cushat sat on two white eggs, in a
latticed nest three feet above the yellow flowers. In the

heart of the thicket, which was dry above the pigeon's tree, with ground cover of creepers and coarse grass tussocks, lay a roe deer doe with three spotted fawns.

The doe was lying hindfoot to forehoof, with head held high, chewing the cud. Her foxy-red coat was dappled with leaf shadows cast by the sun. Close by were her fawns, two sitting face to face licking jet muzzles, and one lying on his side, with legs at full stretch, deep in sleep. Now and again he whimpered and twitched, and each time he whimpered the doe lent her left ear to hearken.

Bounce wakened when the cushat's mate dropped into the hawthorn with a clap-clap-clatter of wings, and sat up with his legs gathered under him. He saw the bird moving sideways along a flowering branch, to take over from her mate who had been sitting on the eggs for more than six hours. When her mate, hopping from the eggs, flapped out and down to skim the pool, he showed no alarm, having learned from the behaviour of his foster-mother that pigeons were not to be feared.

As soon as the cushat had disappeared over the trees, to feed on the tops of unthinned swedes in a field beyond the road, the doe rose slowly to scratch her ears. In the same moment her fawns leaped up and ran to her, eager to nurse. Bounce, who had suckled her twice since his adoption at sunrise, rose to join them. Warm milk and resting sleep had quickly restored his vanished strength, so he was able to hold his place, and oust the buck fawn from the doe's fourth teat before she pulled away to let them know their time was up. While their mother licked rump and cannons, and scratched face and neck with a hindhoof, the fawns went through the ritual of washing each other's faces. Then they wanted to play.

The doe strode slowly from the thicket, cutting deep slots in the wet ground by the pool. Briars clutched at her shoulder, forcing her to turn her head away to protect her eyes. She walked through thick rushes without hesitation, leaped lightly over a knee-high briar, then looked round to see if her family was following.

They were all close behind, copying her gait, in line ahead, with Bounce leading and her own little buck fawn in the rear. When she stopped at the end of the tree cover to sniff, and seek sounds with her ears, they halted dutifully behind her, with ears and noses asking the same questions. Not till she had satisfied herself that no danger lurked beyond her cover, and scanned the foxes' playground, did she move into the open. And then, perhaps because they had sensed some secret signal of permission, the fawns scampered away ahead of her, to skip and dance and caper.

While the doe browsed on leafy twigs of hawthorn and tender shoots of briar, the buck fawns lowered their heads, reared with forelegs stiff, and prepared to butt. The little doe fawn danced away on her own, shaking her head at imaginary opponents, then kicking her heels or rearing with forehooves striking. She danced right to the end of the flat, cutting every caper known to deer, till she kicked herself right off her legs and tumbled down the slope. Undaunted, she danced back up again, to find the doe already halfway across the flat in search of her.

Bounce and Skip soon tired of butting, and backed away from each other tossing their heads. The encounter had been brief, but Skip now realised that his opponent was no longer the weakling of that morning, or the easy antagonist of the early afternoon. During play he liked to be on top so, instead of staying to try other games with Bounce, he skipped away to challenge Dance, his high-stepping sister.

Presently the doe went back to her browsing, snipping off the outermost tips of hawthorn where the leaves were red and tender. Because this was not her main feeding time, she ate only lightly. At this hour she usually lay up in cover. Nightfall and dawn were her favoured times, and she rarely moved about in the open during daylight unless disturbed. But her fawns had to run and play, so she brought them out for brief periods during the day when all was quiet, and it was safe to do so. To this secluded spot she had come to drop them, knowing it was as little disturbed by day as it was by night; and from it she would lead them as soon as they were fit to follow at foot.

A cloud hid the sun for a fleeting moment, and its shadow raced across the ground, followed by light returning. The June day was long, and the sun still four hours from setting. The doe wagged her ears against the flies, while pigeons croodled in the trees across the burn.

Suddenly, she was aware of Bounce beside her. Watching her, he had discovered new cravings still unknown to Skip and Dance, who were yet only seven days old. The doe reached out to him with her soft muzzle, closing her eyes when Bounce licked her face. Then he stepped under her neck, brushing his flank against her knees, to reach for the lowest spray of thorn.

Snatching the first, he pulled sharply, breaking the sappy stem against his lower teeth. He had no front teeth in his upper jaw, in which he was akin to other animals with cleft hooves that chewed the cud. The doe watched for a moment before turning away to bite at tufts of moor grass. Bounce, chewing with quick jaw movements, reached up and snipped off a second leafy twig. Backtracking, with the sprig still protruding from his mouth, and twirling round and round as he gathered it with his lips, he bumped into Dance, who was curious to see what he was doing. Behind her came Skip, blowing after his exertions. Skip reached out with his muzzle to smell what Bounce had in his mouth, sniffing without gripping till the last leaf disappeared. Then he skipped off with Dance butting at his flag.

Blue flowers of brooklime, growing by seeping water, attracted Bounce's attention while he was still chewing on leaves of thorn. He snipped the head from one flower, cutting with the side of his mouth like a dog with a bone, but he passed most of it out again on the other side after slight chewing. After the sweetness of hawthorn, the sharp tang of brooklime didn't appeal to him.

Flies about his head annoyed him little, beyond constantly waggling his ears to keep them off; but, presently, a fly appeared in front of him, hovering with intent, and he jumped back shaking his head. The fly, keeping even distance in front of him, darted to left and right, rising and falling, watching every movement of his head. Panic seized the fawn, and he jumped back and sideways with head held low. The doe, wondering at his antics, loped over to discover the cause.

But she was unable to help, and Bounce couldn't get away from the fly, which seemed determined to pursue him and ignore his mother and sisters. Quick though he was to retreat and evade, he was not quick enough for the persistant fly, which at last found an opening and darted in to squirt a drop of fluid into a left nostril already dilated with fear.

In the fluid were the nostril fly's larvæ, equipped with mouth-hooks to fasten on the membranes of his nostrils till they moved up to burrow in the tissues of his nose. There, if they were successful, they would batten for a year, till he sneezed them out. Then they would go to ground to complete their growth, and emerge as full-winged nostril flies to harass other deer.

The nostril fly's fluid irritated Bounce's nostrils, and he bolted past his foster mother crying in fear. Deeply perplexed, the doe bounded after him. Though she would have shown the same alarm if she had been attacked by the fly, she seemed quite unable to understand what had happened to her fawn. When she at last coaxed him to a standstill she hastened to lick his neck, while he sneezed, and stamped, with a foot, and burrowed his muzzle in the grass.

Then, suddenly, he felt better, and dunted his forehead playfully against his mother's flank.

At first light, three days later, when clouds raced high and the trees tossed wildly after a blustering night of rain, the doe nursed her fawns and prepared to leave the thicket.

In the wet daybreak, birds sang after shaking water from feathers. The cushat on her flat nest rose to claw at ears that itched after much wetting by rain. On the pool, ruffled by the wind, two waterhens appeared, bobbing and bowing, with seven sooty chicks paddling strenuously beside them. Before they vanished among the bending blades of the irises they were caught in a bright beam of light, probing from cloudbanks momentarily rifting.

Water, showering from hawthorns shaken by the wind, dripped on the fawns as they followed the doe from the thicket, into misted rain that webbed their eyes like gossamer. The doe tossed her head irritably, to shake beads of rain from the hair in her ears, and bit at her right shoulder which had been exposed to the weather, and was dark like the hide of a horse that has sweated. Loam and leaf particles, gathered from wet ground, soiled the white fur of her flag, which was also quilled and discoloured where rain had trickled. The fawns' baby spots, hitherto white as snow, had dimmed with soaking, and were now no more than unobtrusive smudges of lighter shade against rain-darkened flanks.

Skip and Dance trotted after the doe, who strode across

the flat with purposeful steps. Before going down into the
hollow, she looked back and saw that Bounce was lagging.
That morning he had nursed without zest, and been
pushed to one side by Skip, who was ever ready to take
advantage of weakness; and now he was swaying on his
legs with the glaze of fever on his eyes. The doe must
have sensed he was ailing, for she returned to touch his
nose with her own, and licked his face with her soothing
tongue. But Bounce made no response to her caress;
instead, he shrank away, as if in fear.

For his brain was hazy, and his legs not his own. There
was a giddiness in his head, caused by the nostril fly's
larvae that had settled in the sinuses of his nose. When he
tried to avoid the doe's solicitous tongue a second time,
his hind legs folded under him and he rolled over on his
side. Rising drunkenly, after much struggling, he staggered away backward with increasing speed till he sat
down on his flag and turned a complete back somersault,
with hooves kicking in the air. Once again he struggled
to his feet, and this time he lurched sideways to collapse in
a heap with all legs splayed. So he gathered his hooves
against his chest and lay panting with tongue showing
over his teeth.

The doe, though impatient to leave, yet sensed that all
was not well with the fawn, and resigned herself to stay.
Lying down close by him, she chewed cud and watched
the other fawns at play.

Rain started to smir, pattering in the trees like mice
feet on rafters. The doe rose to seek cover, but the sudden
krurr-k: krurr-k of the waterhens in the pool froze her in
her tracks, for the call was a warning to chicks which
might have meaning for her. Much of her information
reached her thus indirectly, and she always lent her ears
to birds that raised alarms. The wind being on her flag,
she could get nothing in her nose. But she still wanted to

know. So curiosity delayed her for the verdict of eye or ear. When she heard the plash of feet in shallow, rushy water, she knew without seeing, for her ear could guess what footsteps were making so much noise.

Wheeling, and leaping away in one quick, graceful move, she bounded across the sodden flat with the hair of her flag on end, barking urgent summons to two fawns at play and one lying in a stupor beside a heaving moleheap.

Skip and Dance raced after her, skimming tall grass tussocks that stroked the wet hair of their bellies. Bounce, staggering to his feet, tried to follow, lurching forward drunkenly with his legs playing tricks. But he fell, and lay spreadeagled, and cried like a hare as a bob-tailed cattle dog burst from the pool-side tangles.

The cushat crashing from her nest distracted the dog only for a moment; then she came on with springy steps and bob tail twitching. But the cry that had attracted the dog halted the doe in her slots, instantly, without fore-checking, when she was plunging towards the ridge through meadowsweet bowed with the rain. Almost in the same movement she turned about and leaped away on her own outcoming track, reaching the playground rush-fringe at the same moment as the bitch found Bounce. And she came without her fawns, for both Skip and Dance had dropped when she turned, and were now lying flat among green bracken, with chins pressed close to wet, black loam.

Bounce, lying mute, with long lashes drooped over his eyes, trembled when the bitch weaved close, but made no effort to break. The bitch, circling him and whining, had no thought of molesting him, for such was not her way. He was neither rat, rabbit nor hare, to be killed for sport; nor fox to be chased for the sake of the feud of auld lang syne. She wanted to smell him, and fuss, and perhaps caper and bark, as she did with the calves in the field by

63

the road. So she tried to make him rise by going down on her belly and gurrying at him. It was then she saw the doe.

When a roe is angry, she stamps like a ewe. The doe stamped thrice, jerking up her foot till the knee was tightly bent, then striking the ground sharply with her hoof. She came on six paces and stamped again, with head high and ears pricked forward. The bitch rushed forward to hustle and harass, then read the signs and pulled up to ponder. While she pondered, Bounce bleated once; and the doe, as if at the signal, leaped to the assault.

But the bobtailed bitch knew at once that this was no lumbering heifer beast or glassy-eyed ewe. With bob tail pressed into her buttocks, she shot away as the doe lashed out with her forefeet, a stroke that would have cracked her skull if she had lingered to receive it. She crashed into the rushes without looking back, running with her rump down as if expecting a blow. When she left the rushes, she went up the slope at full speed, with the doe watching her every movement till she disappeared over the rise. For some time afterwards the doe stood at gaze, stamping smartly with a foot because the spring was still in her legs. It was Bounce who brought her mind back to other things, when he rubbed against her, swaying unsteadily as he tried to suck.

Bounce's staggers, or false gid, persisted into the third day, during which time the doe rarely left the thicket by the pool, for they were days of heavy rain, when swallows hunted low among the waterside trees. While the rain lasted she browsed on leaves of briar and sloe and haw-thorn, grazing but little because she had no craving for grass sodden with water. The deer lay under cover by day, moving at nightfall while owls moped on perches, treed by the rain.

The rain ceased at last when wind cleared the sky at

midnight, and the *kee-wicking* and hooting of owls greeted the stars. Water flowed into the pool where the waterhens grunted among the flags. A red stain in the southern sky heralded Mars rising. Musk smell came to the nose of the doe as she nursed her fawns, but she left soon after because the fox was not headed her way. Bounce was now only a little silly, and eager to follow.

On the ridge-top the fawns were on the threshold of a new world. The doe followed the hawthorn hedge through two fields towards the road, snatching at sweet, lobed leaves as she walked. At her heels the fawns walked doucely, in line abreast, being too filled with wonder to caper or stray. The hedgeside growth was thick with hogweed and dock and thistle, and the doe stepped into the knee-high corn to save the strength of her fawns. By the time they reached the road, at an opening in the hedge where two strands of barbed wire were stretched between gateposts, they were soaked to the flanks, with hair plastered to ribs and coats thick with hayseed.

They stopped to scratch and shake coats below the first of Thirteen Beeches growing in line along the roadside hedge—wide-armed, buirdly trees whose roots reached far under the hayfield. Each year, in their branches, nested crow and magpie, who ate the eggs of any cushat that tried to live beside them.

The doe turned left after scratching, travelling on the hard metal road because the verge was a thorny way of briar and trailing bramble, thistle and nettle and fire-weed. Near the main road, she shot up her ears in suspicion when she heard hoof-claps and the bump of wood to the right of the junction. Her route lay straight across and she wanted explanations before moving. More bumps, and a white form appearing at the junction, told her the hoof-claps were a cow's, which was bringing the bumping sound along with it. The cow, with a fence stob tied round her neck to keep her from jumping fences, had just jumped a fence and was hurrying back to the farm where her calf had been taken from her the previous day.

Satisfied that the way was now clear, the doe crossed the road. She had chosen the cross-road route to avoid taking her fawns along the burn, where they would have been soaked through to their skins before reaching the bridge. An owl, with the first mouse in two days pouched comfortably in his craw, hooted and winked as the little herd passed by. Fifty yards from the crossing, the doe jumped through a gap in the hedge into a pasture, to avoid the farm on the bend where she could have crossed the burn by a bridge. The farm was surrounded by tall elms in which rooks were roosting, and there lived two greyhounds whose savagery she feared.

The cows in the pasture trotted after the deer to the fence above the burn, and a hedgehog, hunting under the wire, coiled into an armoured ball when he heard them coming. He didn't uncoil until the cows had turned back and the deer were across the burn, and then he found a peewit chick, killed by a hoof, which he ate on the spot.

At the bank top, on the other side of the burn, the family halted while their mother tested the wind. Though she knew that men were unlikely to be abroad at such an hour, she was taking no chances. Curiosity was her weakness; not lack of caution. She had lived long enough to know that men turned up in the most unexpected places at the most unlikely times.

Finding nothing with her nose, she continued on her way, crossing pastures and rootfields, but skirting fields of hay and corn. At Stane Farm she met a fox leaving with a hen in his jaws, and stamped her foot while the fawns huddled close to her flank. From there she travelled by the Wood-of-no-name to Fin-me-oot Cottage, where

Bounce's sister slept in a dog basket on the kitchen floor.
In the orchard she bit off two leaves from one of Patrick's
Ribston Pippins, before forcing her way through the
hedge into the rough, rush-grown field where curlews
nested.

With the fawns crowding her close, she hastened across
the field, reaching the neck of heather on the far side
without any salute from the watchful curlews, who would
have risen for dog or fox but had no interest in deer. The
heather neck was narrow, and the little herd soon reached
the moor road to Glencryan. One field beyond, a dark
mass in the gloaming, was Dryflatts Wood, which was her
destination. At two o'clock in the morning she led her
family into the larch gloom, having travelled two miles
and three-quarters from the thicket by the pool.

The fawns slept while Capella, blazoning, mounted his
starry chariot to herald the quick-returning sun, and other
stars, which were the eyes of a fox, flickered crimson in
the larch gloom.

They woke when cushat wings buffeted in the feathery
tops at dawn, rising and arching their back while the doe
lay quietly under down-spreading branches chewing the
cud. Tufter, the long-eared owl, flew in on noiseless wings
with the first larksong, and sat on a low branch staring at
them with his brilliant eyes. For five years he had lived,
and nested, in Dryflatts, rearing seventeen owlets who
had eaten more than seven hundred mice, voles, shrews
and rats before they were able to perch on branches.

By the time Tufter had raised his ear tufts, which he
kept down in flight, Bounce had lost interest in him, and
was ready to nurse. When the doe rose to give them suck,
he was first at her flank and first to find her udder, and
butted Skip aside when the milk was dwindling. Tufter
sighed *Oo-oo-oo-oo*, breathlessly, blinking his eyes. The

doe, stepping clear of her family, nosed each in turn, before striding away through the larches. Whether she had conveyed some command, or whether they knew without telling, they made no attempt to follow. Instead, they scraped beds with forehooves and lay down quietly to await her return.

The stars paled as the sky brightened, but no light reached the sleeping fawns. There, under the dense canopy, where noonday was twilight, sunshine was no more than golden arrows piercing the gloom, or pools of light where wind-blows leaned. Branches and larch sheddings layered the ground carpet, and rabbits lived in brushwood heaps where no ferns grew. Shells of cushat eggs—some veined with dried blood to show chicks had emerged; some clear that had been sucked by crows—were scattered on the ground beside feathers loosened from breasts when the cushats fought their way into the dense larch tops.

When the doe returned, the sun was up, and gulls were flying across a sky of speedwell blue, where vapour clouds trailed like feathers blown by the wind. Bounce, hearing her with his left ear, jumped and ran to her, calling *Eep-eep. Eep-eep. Nee-eep!* Tufter, opening orange eyes in which jet pupils were contracting, winked, then rolled down his lids. Making low noises in her throat, the doe wheeled in her tracks, and the fawns followed her by the way she had come. Soon they were clear of the larches, among tall pines where their eyes were dazzled by the probing rays of the sun, and there the doe met the antlered buck she had sought and found while her fawns were sleeping.

With the buck leading, the deer filed into the big pasture which reached like a grassy bay into the hardwood fringe of Dryflats. Peewits were running among the thistles and ragwort, feeding when they stopped to tilt forward on unbending legs. A cock pheasant, flying out over the heads of the deer, bounced and skipped at the touchdown, then sprinted away with erect tail to feed on buttercup heads and clover. At the field bottom, where the ground dipped to the glen, cows were grazing out of the ground mist that hid rabbits advancing in line behind them.

Overawed by the buck, who had so mysteriously appeared to join them, the fawns kept close to their mother. The buck, having taken charge, was content to ignore them. He was the father of Skip and Dance, which they had no way of knowing, and would never know.

The fawns played, but kept close to the doe, moving with her as she grazed towards the hayfield fence. She pulled at short grass and long grass, clover, self-heal and dandelion, without eating to repletion on any. Presently, craving still further variety, she moved to the wood edge, to try rank grass and stitch-wort and dock, and browse on thorn and beech and briar. The buck joined her while she was reaching for oak leaves, and together they moved down the hedge.

Bounce, lingering behind to lip hawthorn shoots, was startled when a plump, brown bird slipped from under an archway of grass, and raced down the hedge-side clucking like a hen with chicks. He watched her for a moment before turning back to nibble, but before he had chewed two mouthfuls of thorn leaves the dumpy bird came back, followed by her mate, who had a chestnut horseshoe on his breast. The birds took no notice of him, though he reached down to smell, and entered the archway of grass with their heads held low. Bounce could hear them chuckling in the hedgebottom, but had no thought of prying. The partridge's eggs were hatching, and she had gone to summon her mate so that he could take the chicks under his wing as they arrived, and brood half of them when the whole family was out.

When he went to rejoin his mother, Bounce found the fawns tasting thorn leaves, while the buck was eating bramble. Bounce bit at snakeweed, which had pink flowers on long stems and leaves like common dock. Discovering he liked the taste, he ate a leaf and a half. When the buck reached down with his muzzle, the fawn touched it tentatively with his own, for the smell was reassuring and his mother was watching nearby. Finding the stranger friendly, he sniffed at an antler, and ate another leaf and a half.

Doe and fawns lay up in the larches for the day, while the buck sought his own harbour among bushy birch scrub in a hollow nearby. The fawns slept and played at intervals, under the thick larches where the ground was clear, and were suckled four times by the doe before the wood grew dark. When the sun was a red glare in a mist of purple, and the near hills deep indigo under a clear sky, they were led by their mother to the morning pasture, where the buck was already grazing beside an ambling hare. And they spent the short, twilit night in the open, playing, resting, nursing or nibbling, till the pheasants crowed in Dryflatts and a man and dog arrived to herd the cows for the milking.

So the days passed quietly till midsummer, with the doe taking her fawns farther and farther out, till they had trodden every deer path in Dryflatts and the surrounding fields. They were variable days of sun and wind and rain, with starlit nights, and nights of thick mist when woodcock were silent, and owls mewed or wailed in complaint. Bounce, his stature increasing daily, was the most robust fawn of the trio, as well as the most boisterous, and his wild cantrips were soon too much for little Dance, who always ran to her mother when his play became too rough.

Even the doe was harassed by him when he persisted in dunting her flank or boring under her forelegs with his head.

Then, gradually, their placid life changed. The buck, haughty and high-stepping, began to stay close by day and night, and to pay amorous court to the doe. His attitude to the fawns became one of cool indifference. One morning he barked, and stabbed savagely at a pine tree with his antlers, tearing away bark till his dags were tipped with sticky resin. The barking was not new, for by then Bounce had heard his mother yapping like a dog, in warning or to keep in touch at night. But the buck barked frequently and for no clear reason, and often stamped with a foot as if in anger.

When the hay was cut, and the night air sweet with its perfume, Bounce heard another buck barking in Dryflatts, but, though he heard grunting afterwards, and a sound like the rattling of dry sticks, he had no knowledge of what was afoot.

In the weeks following midsummer, the fawns steadily increased their range, for their mother was now siezed by a commanding restlessness, and led them farther and farther afield from Dryflatts. One morning they rested within sight of Glencryan, half a mile from their harbour. Yet their world was still small, and most of their time was spent within easy running distance of their own wood.

Each day they browsed and grazed more and more; and each day the spots on their coats grew fainter. The doe began to disappear every morning at sunrise, leaving the fawns couched in Dryflatts while she went to join the buck on the moor edge. On certain days she travelled there at sunset as well. One morning she allowed them to follow her, but she put them down in thick heather two hundred yards from her trysting place. Bounce, rising once, saw her running round a birch tree that grew among moor grass, pursued by the buck who was the father of Skip and Dance. Mystified, he lay down to wait for her, while larks sang and a merlin quartered the heather.

In August, when the heather was numerous with bees, and curlews gathered on the moor, the buck disappeared, and the old order was restored. By then, the fawns' spots had disappeared as well.

7

FROM A SKY OF BLUE GLASS THE SUN BREATHED FIRE
on the moor. Bees, with rainbows in their wings,
clustered on the heather like raindrops, harvesting the
sweet nectar. Heather-honey scent lay heavy on the air,
distilled by the sun. Swallows from Firknowe Farm,
hidden behind the spinney across the loch, hawked low
over the purple tops, snatching crane flies and hover flies
from clouds of yellow pollen.

Up in the luminous blue, out of reach of the hot waves
of air that ruffled the heather, Kyack the falcon circled
in the sun-glare, now wheeling, now drifting, now flashing across the glassy sky with a mighty surge of wings. Up
there, the air was cool and hunger-making; a relief from
the torrid heat of his perch among the ruins of Hoolet
Nest steading, where he had fretted, open-beaked, till his
throat was dry.

Kyack flicked his wings and made a steep right-hand
turn, sweeping round with the sun on his back. His hard,
bright eyes, fierce under their flat crowns, scanned the
ground and the lower spaces of air for grouse or duck or
pigeon or unsuspecting plover. Far below, he could see
gulls on the water, dipping heads and flapping wings
among the dancing highlights. In the shallows, the
Firknowe cattle stood belly deep, with heads bowed
meekly under the assault of flies. But there was no movement above the heather; in the stifling heat all likely prey
was earthbound.

For a moment, Kyack hovered like a kestrel; then he

73

climbed towards the sun to drift at a still higher pitch. From there, his fierce, far-seeing eyes looked down on rolling acres that had seen two thousand years of history. To the north, the hills seemed afloat on the shimmering air—tawny-yellow on the crests, violet in the glens and gullies, glowing purple on the slopes where heather grew. Away to his left he could see Stirling Castle, a grim bastion dominating the wide carse lands, and Wallace's Monument, towering above the historic field where the Guardian of Scotland shattered proud Cressingham and the feudal chivalry of England. Closer still lay the field of Bannockburn, where once the great war horses neighed when Bruce forever blunted the sword of England, and where still the ghostly knights of Edward fall at bat-light each midsummer eve. . . .

Three carrion crows rose from the wood beside the keeper's cottage to harry the falcon as he turned high above the canal near the main north road; but his angry scream sent them down to think again. While they circled below, snarling and *harring*, the falcon turned away from the canal at speed to return to Hoolet Nest, losing height as he flew.

Kyack swung wide round the ruin to make one more scouting circuit before flying down to roost, but this time he quartered the ground at high speed and at little more than three hundred feet. On that final sweep he saw a hare dawdling among the strewn feathers and empty nests of the gullery, a hoodie crow perched on a grouse butt inside the heather line, and four roe deer couched by a gnurly birch beside a peat hag. At the loch he checked and turned when he spied three men with guns, and two springer spaniels, coming round the shore. It was then he realised he still had his escort of three carrion crows.

When he turned back across the heather he started to

climb, and the crows, knowing nothing of his kind,
climbed after him. For Kyack was a wanderer, passing
through, and the crows that dwelt on the moor had
neither knowledge of him, nor inherited wisdom. To
them, he was simply a bigger version of the little mousing
kestrel, to be harried and chivvied as they pleased. Up, up,
he went, with the crows following, but falling farther and
farther behind. Then, suddenly, Kyack turned, tilted
forward, and shot down with a mighty thrust of wings.

Down he came in a vertical dive, at terrific speed, with
wings half closed—a meteor in blue and ermine, a rushing
thunderbolt of feathers—the king of all the falcons. The
crows squawked and broke away, alive at last to the peril.
But—too late! The deer in the heather heard the thud
of the impact. Black feathers tossed on the air as the
falcon spread his wings and swept upwards after his stoop.
The wings of the nearest crow went slack. For a moment
its open beak, with tongue protruding, pointed to the
sky; then the body crumpled and fell, to crash beside the
deer in the heather below.

While Kyack threw up to gain height for a second
assault the deer jumped to their feet, startled by the thing
that had fallen from the sky. The little herd of doe and
three fawns stood taut, with white flags spread in alarm,
ready for instant flight if the body in the heather moved.
But the crow didn't move, and the sprawled wings, and
scarlet threads trickling over sheened, blue-black feathers,
showed it would never move again. The doe, suddenly
aware that the thing was nothing more than a dead bird,
nudged her fawns to reassure them while the white disk
of her flag contracted. When she lay down again, the
fawns couched close by her with confidence restored.

Bounce, lying within tongueing distance of his foster-
mother, watched crows and falcon circling overhead, with
ears tuned to their cries. He saw the falcon overshoot

with his second dive, then swing up to bind on to a yar-ring crow from below, turning over on his back as he struck with his knife-edged talons. The crow, clutched in a foot of steel, rasped out his last strangled cry, and presently another body fell limp to the ground. When Kyack shot away in pursuit of the third crow, Bounce could see them no longer, for his eyes were not far-seeing. So he knew nothing of the drama enacted above Hoolet Nest, where a third crow, with its throat almost torn out, crashed into the grass-grown kitchen of the ruined steading, followed down by a falcon with bloody feet.

At noon the birch leaves wilted and curled inwards with the blast furnace heat of the sun, and even the heather tips drooped. The deer, tortured by the hot gusts of air, panted audibly, with tongues lolling and flanks heaving. The fawns' coats, sheened and silky with much scorching, showed vague outlines of their vanished spots in the harsh light. The doe rose when Dance, greatly distressed by the relentless heat, tried to bury herself in the heather, and set off in the direction of Firknowe Spinney with all three at her heels.

The hoodie on his grouse butt saw the herd approach-ing, and *kwarped* his greeting, puffing his throat and low-ering his head. The doe ignored his comments, though she should have listened to his advice, for when Smoky Joe gave warnings all wise things lent their ears. At the moment she had no interest in him. Apart from respect for his judgement, she felt only distrust, for she knew the hoodie would peck the eyes from a new-born fawn or take her own if she were ailing. But Joe was well fed, and in bantering mood, and danced on his perch like a buffoon to show he had no evil intentions.

At that moment a dog barked in Firknowe. The crow stopped clowning and the doe pricked her ears. Bounce, his slim legs dusty with yellow pollen, copied her pose and stamped with a foot. The crow, dismissing the sound, said *Harr-rr* to show it was of no importance. But, to the doe, the barking meant a change of plans. Firknowe was now out of the question, yet she was reluctant to lead her fawns across two gruelling miles of heather to reach the ample shade of Glencryan or Dryflatts. It was Bounce who solved her dilemma, by walking into the butt and throwing himself down in the shade of a heather wall buttressed with peat and branches.

Smoky Joe, with head cocked and eyes shining like ripe blackberries, watched intently while they scraped with forehooves to prepare their lies. Dance joined Bounce on the inside, pounding at woody heather twigs, charred with old fires, till she had cleared a patch for her hip. When the doe and Skip were settled, muzzle to muzzle on the outside, Smoky Joe sidled round the top of the butt till he was above Bounce's head. He poked his ebony pick-axe beak between his feet and chuckled in his throat. With neck feathers on end, he pulled silver-crusted tips of dead heather from between his black toes, vibrating his tail as he did so. Then he flew down beside Bounce and said *Kwarp: ha-harr.*

Bounce shrank away, not because he was afraid, but because he had a strong ancestral suspicion of all crows, and wanted room to manoeuvre in case of attack. But when the old crow treated him to an elaborate display he reached out to smell him. With beak to ground and breast feathers puffed over his toes, the bird chortled and chuckled, with lifted wings and spread tail vibrating rapidly, as a hen owl does when her mate brings prey to the nest in the night. Bounce watched wide-eyed till Smoky Joe stopped to shake himself, then touched the bird's ash-grey breast with his muzzle. The crow leaped back squawking at the contact, and Bounce jumped to his feet, lowering his head in challenge.

77

Joe *kwarped* mockingly before dancing away to poke in a corner of the butt, grumbling in his throat as he thrust his glossy head into the packed, brittle heather. Presently he pulled out a piece of rotten mutton, one of many he had hidden in the butt for future use, for the old crow was provident and, unlike the squirrels, remembered all his hiding places. With his mouth full of mutton, he looked up to find Bounce prodding air, with hindlegs braced as if he was meeting resistance. After much elaborate bowing and tail fanning Joe dropped his titbit, then crouched down behind it like a dog that seeks a quarrel over a bone.

Getting no response to his taunt, he skipped over suddenly and nipped Bounce on a foreleg. Bounce retaliated by mincing forward with head held low; but when he tried to prod he was promptly tweaked in an ear. But this time the crow had gone too far; for the fawn, stung to anger, reared up and struck out with a forehoof. Had the stroke made contact Smoky Joe would have been a cripple, for that tiny hoof had an edge like a knife. Instead, it merely bent his tail feathers, so he flapped up to the top of the butt before the deer could strike again.

With his tormentor out of reach Bounce went round behind the butt to seek solace in the company of his mother. He found her sleeping on her side, with legs outstretched, her flanks rising and falling in rhythm with her breathing. Skip, too, was asleep, with his muzzle resting on his mother's hocks. Bounce licked the doe's white chin till she opened her eyes and withdrew her leg from under Skip's chin. Then she rose to give them suck, while the crow, once more inside the butt, went through the ritual of hiding his mutton, wedging it in a corner and covering it with a tiny heap of dry peat, heather stems and crusted lichen.

After thirty seconds the doe took two steps forward, thus forcing the fawns' heads from under her. Bounce stepped back as Smoky Joe trailed low over the heather, to pitch, squawking, beside a ditch less than thirty yards away. With a vigorous shake of his head the fawn gave chase, jumping six feet to the left, then six to the right, and kicking his heels with his head held low. He found Smoky Joe perched on the exposed ribs of a long-dead sheep. Green, frayed wool clung matted to ribs bleached by weathering and discoloured by the feet of many birds, and two horns were showing above the green slime on the peaty water.

The crow was holding in his beak a black and orange beetle which he had picked from the body of the sheep. Scores of other beetles were working under the braxie, trying to undermine it before they laid their eggs in the flesh. Joe crushed his captive as he turned to face the fawn, and swallowed it without distaste; which showed how little he thought of theories, for sexton beetles are supposed to be unpalatable and strikingly coloured to protect them from attack.

Bounce lowered his head, pranced, and launched himself at the crow. He was no longer angry, but prepared to play rough. The hoodie, over-confident, left his evading jump too late, and was struck before his wings had got a grip on the air. But he was allowed to recover when Bounce danced back to work up to a second assault. When the second rush came he was inside the braxie's ribs sorting out his wits. When Bounce made the mistake of sniffing too close he was bitten savagely on the chin, which made him realise that he had no answer to a crow's beak stabbing through the open ribs of a sheep. So he went back to his mother, his inborn distrust of all hoodies confirmed by painful experience.

In the shade of the butt he lay chewing cud, close to his mother with his rump against Skip's flank, while gauzy-winged bees whined past in a constant stream, carrying the heather harvest to the long line of hives on the flat loch shore. His cud chewing was methodical—two movements of the lower jaw to the right, and the remainder to the left, till the mouthful was swallowed. When the next mouthful came up, showing as a ripple on the satin skin of his neck, he repeated the process. At regular intervals of six or seven regurgitations he changed the order, chewing first to the left instead of the right; but the number was always the same—two in one direction, the remainder on the other side.

He was licking his shoulder when Smoky Joe flapped down at the entrance to the butt. But this time the crow was nervous, and his nervousness was somehow conveyed to Bounce's mother, for she jumped suddenly to her feet with head high and ears cupped forward. The crow snipped yellow flowers of tormentil and tossed them over his shoulder, then, with a harsh caw, flew low over the heather towards the stunted pines of Hoolet Nest. The fawns watched the doe, tensed to break; but still she stood, head up, ears twitching, sensing peril yet unable to identify or place it.

Then, suddenly, the tension was broken. The doe barked urgently, and broke away. Behind her a covey of red grouse exploded into the air, to come hurtling after her in tight formation on down-curved wings. Shotguns roared as three men with dogs appeared over a rise a hundred yards from the butt. Two grouse faltered in flight, flapped wings broken with No. 5 shot, and fell on a slant; a second towered and crumpled, beak to breast, before pitching down to hit the heather in a cloud of feathers. The rest of the pack whirred close on the heels of the fleeing deer, almost breasting the heather tops, while the spaniels were waved out to collect dead and find wounded.

But one of the springers, seeing the deer, had a mind to

chase them, and raced after them yelping while men swore and blew recalls in vain. Heat and high heather soon tired the dog, and he turned when he realised he had no hope of catching the deer. While he sneaked back, to be cuffed and sent out to quest, the deer bounded in headlong flight towards Hoolet Nest, with the fawns following in line behind the doe. The ground was new to them so they ran in her slots. Round dubs of peat, over lichened, heather-crowned boulders, across treacherous water channels topped with sphagnum, the waywise doe led her family without faltering. And presently they reached the great sheugh that bordered the rush-grown Hoolet Nest pastures.

The sheugh, or great ditch, deep, with sheer peat sides, was four feet wide and no obstacle to deer that knew the ground. But in front of it the ground rose to a foot high bank half as wide as the sheugh. The doe jumped from the bank top, sailed up and over, and touched down on the far side with three feet to spare. From the spot slotted by her take-off Bounce leaped unhesitatingly, with forehooves held to his breast and hind legs rigid after the thrust. Landing with inches to spare, he bounded after the doe without slackening pace. Close behind him jumped Dance, who stumbled as she landed. She was on her feet when Skip left the ground. The doe, halting to make sure her fawns were following, saw two running her line, then heard a wild cry from the third; for Skip was in the ditch, having jumped too soon because he thought he had only the bank to clear.

Alarmed, the doe turned back, with white flag spread. From the lip of the sheugh she looked down on her fawn, standing neck deep in dark peaty water, and wailing piteously like a hare in a snare or in the grip of a collie's teeth. The fawn leaped at sight of his mother, furrowing the wet peat with his forehooves; but the ditch was too deep and he fell over backwards with his head under water. Struggling to his feet with much splashing, he coughed the water from his lungs, while the doe, pawing at the top, sent down showers of dry peat that blinded him.

In a panic the doe started to trot along the bank. Skip, afraid she was deserting him, tried to keep pace, plunging and leaping and falling, gulping water when he fell, coughing and drooling when he rose. Peat flinders swirled in the dark, cool water; a fat water vole, nibbling at a rush stem on a narrow spit of peat, fled from the disturbance, escaping to its burrow near the top by tracks no deer could follow.

The doe turned where the sheugh was spanned by a little bridge built of turves and birch poles, which was a crossing place used by foxes. Retracing her steps at a smarter pace, she reached her starting place, and turned again. And so she carried on, rushing up and down, always turning at the bridge of turf. If she had kept on for a hundred yards she could have got the fawn out where the ground was level and the ditch no more than a ribbon of water. But, like a hen confronted with a barrier of netting, she galloped up and down on a short beat, till the fawn in the ditch was exhausted and barely able to keep his head above the water.

Skip was trapped, for he was only a little fawn, twenty inches high at the shoulder, standing helpless in two feet of water, with three feet of sheer ditch wall above him. To the August drought he owed his life, for in normal seasons the rains spilled five feet of chill water into the sheugh, and death would have been a matter of seconds. As it was, he was barely able to stand; he was choking and glassy of eye; and his mother was quite unable to help him.

Men and dogs walking towards the bridge of turf, with

three grouse in the game bag and two spaniels casting ahead, sent the doe's ears up when she had made her twentieth run along the sheugh. Men were the last things she could have wished for at that moment, yet they were the only beings able to help her fawn. But such understanding was beyond the powers of the doe, who saw in them only additional peril. So she barked, with flag spread full, and trotted away a little distance, with Bounce and Dance at her side.

The doe started running in circles as the men approached the sheugh, while Bounce and Dance dropped to the ground in obedience to her gruff bark of command. Skip, wailing heartbrokenly, attracted the dogs, and the dogs, barking their discovery to the men, raced to the sheugh. In her frenzy of fear the doe cut in closer, till she was running her circle barely sixty yards from the dogs, barking her summons to a fawn who couldn't follow.

John Long, the keeper, wearing a braw suit of tweeds and a shirt of Cameron tartan, was the first to reach the sheugh. Laying down the game bag, he called off the dogs, and coupled them before looking into the ditch. When he lay down on his belly to peer over the edge, the fawn stood still, shilpet and shivering, and too weak to move.

Long called to his shooting companions to hurry and lend a hand, while the dogs, bobbing on their seats, were warned "Down! Damn ye! Down!"

"A roe kid droonin' in the sheugh," he said, when his son Willie arrived with the laird. "If ye tak me by the feet I'll mebbe manage tae fish it oot."

So they held him by the ankles, and lowered him over the edge. Long's shirt and green tweed jacket were plastered with wet peat before he got his hands on the fawn. Skip, almost indifferent to the touch, allowed himself to be pulled by the neck, then grasped by the forelegs. Only when he was hoisted from the ditch, held firmly in John Long's arms, did he strike out with a forefoot in a last despairing struggle. The blow took the keeper on the cheek, bruising the bone and cutting the skin, which bled on the instant.

"Damn!" said Long, hurriedly dropping the fawn. "I should hae kent better!"

"That might have been your eye . . ." the laird began. "Take care Willie," he shouted, as the boy knelt to grasp the fawn by the legs. But there was no need for care, for Skip was lying on his side, his tongue protruding from the side of his mouth, his lip drawn back from his lower teeth, his breathing a snort and his mouth oozing water.

"Look at the auld deer," said Willie, pointing to the doe, who was still bounding on her anxious circuit, barking at intervals.

"Well, sir," said Long to the laird, "this beast's aboot loused. Micht as well chap it on the heid noo and be done wi' it. It'll mak a grand bait for foxes and hoodies."

The laird turned Skip over with his foot, and found the slim body slack. "Leave it to her," he said at last, "then she'll know. You can do what you like with it in the morning."

But Long was stubborn. "As you say, sir," he said, "but if the foxes come on it the nicht there'll be little mair than banes gin dalight."

The laird, however, was insistent. The doe didn't know her fawn was dead and the laird, being a man of some imagination and understanding, wanted to leave her to certainty and mourning. Long, who was a remarkable man in many ways, lacked the finer nuances of imagination, and thought the laird was being stubborn. His son, quite frankly, thought he was daft, although he didn't say so.

So they left, with the dogs in hand, walking quickly to allow the doe to tryst with her dead.

Yet, if they could have been present half an hour later, they would have witnessed a strange scene, when the doe returned to her fawn. Standing over him, she made low noises in her throat, then gently licked his soaking muzzle. Twice she snorted in his face, all the while tapping him lightly with a caressing, polished forehoof, as if bidding him rise and follow. And, if they had been present later still they would have seen her, as Kyack saw her, when she entered the Hoolet Nest pines with three fawns at foot.

8

THE LAST GOLDEN STARS OF BOG ASPHODEL FADED ON the moor. Misty daybreaks followed still, clear nights of heavy dew; but the sun lifted the mists each morning, and the hazed sky cleared like a lens that is polished. By day the moor wilted in waves of heat, and the western sky was a blaze of fire at the sun's departing.

Grouse, starved of water, flocked to the wet ground near Glencryan, returning to the open moor each sunset to cram their crops with green shoots of heather. The gangrel falcon left Hoolet Nest to continue his wanderings, after killing three grouse and being shot at by John Long when the keeper came to collect a dead fawn that was not. The doe left Hoolet Nest the following daybreak, reluctantly because it was her habit to live out on the heather for some weeks after the rut, but prompted by the obvious distress of her fawns. The Hoolet Nest pines afforded scant cover and Skip, still shaky on his legs, was the chief sufferer.

The deer took the direct route from the heather to Glencryan, crossing the narrow moor road to the wood before the sun won through. On the roadside verge grew harebell and cat's ear; and yellow and purple vetch which farmers call fitches and roe deer like to eat. Purple heads of knapweed, shaped like flowers of thistle, grew higher than the rumps of the fawns. From a tall stand of fireweed at the woodside ditch came an old boar badger, who grunted at the deer before shambling down the verge to his crossing place beside a beech with many stems and ferns growing in a crotch.

When the badger had gone, to seek a late bed after lingering overlong digging for earthnuts, the deer snatched hastily at vetch and harebell, ignoring tall seeding hogweed and white-flecked leaves smelling strongly of liquorice. Presently the doe walked away, chewing on jointed stems of vetch. Bounce was first on her heels, following her on the badger's trail, and jumping the ditch at her side into the shoulder-high blaeberries of Glencryan. Skip, afraid of the leap, trotted with Dance on the outside to take the badger's route across, joining the others under the screening hazels.

From the hazels a well marked deer path led away into the pines. It was the trail taken by Bounce's mother when she made her last journey to Heatherfield to give birth to her fawns; a route followed by generations of roe in their daily lives, and in their comings and goings between the heather line and the wooded farmlands to the west. Sheep used the track when they were shifting ground; foxes trotted along it when heather and blaeberries and bog cotton were drenched; and it was regularly walked by John Long himself as the best route through Glencryan.

Before taking the trail the doe reached up to browse on leaves of hazel, wagging her ears and kicking with a hindfoot against the gathering flies. The fawns, at first, sought blaeberries, chewing on the stems with the side of their mouths, or clipping off sprigs with a jerk of their heads. In a few moments Bounce joined his mother, after spitting out the dead, shrunken body of a big emperor moth which he had gathered in with a mouthful of leaves. The swelling hazel nuts, like pallid acorns clasped in green, attracted him at once; so he reared on his hindlegs, with forehooves against his chest, and tried to reach them. But the lowest nuts eluded his questing muzzle, and he dropped to all fours again, curling tongue over nostrils to betray his hankering.

87

A crow *cra-aa-ed* harshly as the doe turned to go, and she kept touch with an ear till she was clear of the first belt of pines. In the heather clearing sheep were grazing—blackface ewes with fat lambs at foot. The deer left their runway to avoid mixing with the sheep, crossing to the second pine neck through belly-high heather that clawed the sheened, satin skin of their legs. Forking back to her runway, the doe broke into a trot, with one ear laid back for the voice of the crow and the other directed forward to the beeches ahead. Once among the tall, canopied beeches where the leaf-filtered light was soft and concealing, they slowed to a walk, the fawns treading in the doe's tracks because they were not waywise in the wood.

They found their lies among brushwood and creepers where a great oak tree grew on the fringe of the beech-wood, driving out a hare who had a form pressed in the loam in the heart of the tangle. The hare ambled clear without fuss, then sat up to look back, with black-tipped ears erect and cleft lips quivering over his big, yellow teeth. He scratched the back of his head with a hairy hindfoot as the doe went down on her knees. By the time he disappeared beyond the beeches the deer were settled in their harbour, their rumps towards the sunrise, their coats barred and dappled in the broken light. Bounce licked the hair of his right shoulder, revealing an undercoat of blue in the wake of his tongue, while his mother, with one eye closed, lick-licked in the cleft of a forehoof. Then they all closed eyes in sleep.

Twice, during the bright daylight, the fawns rose to nurse and bite at beech leaves, while cushats *coo-coo-rooed* drowsily in the heat and owls dozed on northside branches in dense spruce tops. Bounce butted with Skip when the sun was red. They circled head to head, muzzles pressed to knees and hindhooves furrowing the deap leaf mould. Pigeon wings whistling above the beeches sent them back to the doe, for not yet had they learned that cushats flying in to roost convey a different message from those clattering out in alarm. When the first bird flapped into the oak, with dirt on his beak and thirteen hundred wheat berries in his crop, the doe jumped to her feet and licked the inside of a foreleg. Then an owl hooted and it was time for her to go.

They went first to drink, from a pebbly pool under a peat overhang on the edge of the wood. The doe sucked water steadily, with little noise; but the fawns drank, snorting, like calves taking milk from a pail. Two cushats flapped down as the doe stepped back with chin dripping water, thrusting their beaks in to the eyes and drinking their fill in one long draught. A big owl, with a big head, made two swift circuits of the beechwood as the deer walked slowly along the edge. It was One Eye, the Glencryan tawny owl, who had been stabbed in the left eye by a magpie when he fell during his first flight after striking a branch. One Eye pitched on a mossed, barkless stump, and clicked his hooked beak at the passing deer. When they were clear of the beeches he flew away on noiseless wings to hunt voles among the blaeberries.

The deer snipped leaves along the woodside—hawthorn and willow and hazel, and rough, rasping leaves of elm. A great, red-faced moon, eyebrowed and moustached with three wisps of lilac cloud, came up as the sun went down, and the air grew chill. A woodcock crossed the moon's face in wavering flight as the deer stepped into the shadow of a half-uprooted horse chestnut. Hard against the upturned roots a big fox was lying, biting viciously at fleas in his fur. Fox and roe noted each other without malice, and the fox went on with his flea hunt when the deer cantered away along a twisting path to the other side of the wood.

The moon became honey-coloured, then silvered as the

light faded in the west. Rabbits moved out from Glen-cryan to the Stane Farm pasture as bats winged from the cobwebby stable rafters to hawk flies above the woodside trees. The deer stepped into the pasture with the first of the rabbits and started to graze in the tree shadows cast by the moon. They could hear One Eye yelping three fields away as he hunted mice on the stubble, and the far cangling of gulls as they settled to roost on the loch. Half an hour later they lay down among tall grass and dogrose to rest and chew cud.

When the moon was four hours old they left for Stane Farm, accompanied by their shadows as they crossed the open fields. Within gunshot of the stackyard deer and shadows disappeared in the darkness of trees. The farm was still in the moonlight; no lights showed in the windows; and the heavy shadows of chestnut trees by the threshing shed lay dark across the yard. The doe hearkened to the hiss and gurgle of water from a tap by the stable door, and the contented grunting of the pigs in their sty, then jumped the stackyard fence into a foggage field rich with the smell of knee-high clover. It was then she heard a new sound—the rumbling growl of a dog; and in a moment she heard the rush of his feet in the grass.

The doe barked and bounded away with head held high. Obeying her signal at once, the fawns skimmed clover in her tracks, their open flags betraying their line of flight. But the dog, instead of following, was content to cast around feathering where the deer had stood. He was a callow collie pup, growing to be a watchdog; but he had no interest in deer other than stampeding them from harbour or grazing. On his way back to his barrel kennel he stopped at the midden to dig up a hen he had killed that morning. He cast furtive glances at the kitchen as he dug, for he had been kicked and pelted with potatoes at the time of the killing, and feared he might be caught again.

At the Wood-of-no-name the deer stopped short in their slots, realising that the dog wasn't following. But, in a moment, they were forced to run again, when the Stane Farm dairy herd came shambling down upon them, led by a yearling Ayrshire bull with an abiding hatred of deer. The doe moved leisurely, content to keep clear; but when the bull lunged at her viciously she leaped away in a panic, barking to her fawns. They crashed into the wood, sending up the pigeons and startling a man walking on the road in the light of the moon. The pigeons whistled above the trees as the cows stopped short at the fence. By the time they clattered back to roost the man on the road had seen the bull stab twenty fence stobs with his horns.

In a grove of dark spruces, close-set among spacious pines, the deer stopped to pant and wag ears. Overhead, right and left, they heard the rubbing of feet and the dry scrape of claws on perches. The rubbing was pheasant; the scraping was owl. From the scraper's perch came suddenly *Hoo-oo-oh*, so low pitched and gentle that it was almost a sigh; then an owl flapped noiselessly into the face of the moon. The pheasant crowed and crashed through spruce twigs, and droppings pattered at the deer's feet, followed by drifting breast feathers.

The whistle of the pheasant's wings died away. From all over the wood came the throaty queries of a dozen others. Soon the pigeons settled and the wood became quiet. Footsteps on the road were quickly beyond hearing. The doe licked her brisket and scratched her neck with a hindfoot. Then she lay down with her fawns in the damp gloom of the spruces.

At first light they left the wood, by way of the broken gate, which was still attached to its post by one rust-eaten hinge held by one rusted nail. A chill wind was rising as they picked their way down the bracken-covered slope to the burn. Vapour lying on the water hid the deer as they crossed. It also hid Brock, the badger, where he was digging out a wasp's bike under roots in the bank. Brock's mouth was full of paper and wasp grubs which he chewed with noisy delight. In his fur and on his face were scores of cold-drowsy wasps, whose stings he accepted stoically as part of the price. He grunted once at the deer, then went on with his digging, making the dark loam fly with his black, bear-like claws.

Magpies were shuggying in the dawn light when the deer reached Patrick MacPherson's orchard, where rabbits were grazing on the goose-cropped grass under the apple trees. Partridges were running head down in the hedge-bottom, *krooking* and making a noise like a key turning in a rusty lock. Bounce bit at a small green apple which he found in the grass, and loosened a tooth without being able to cut the tough skin. So he spat out the tooth, and left the apple to his mother, and searched among the trees till he found a ripe plum. He ate the plum and four others, rolling them round in his mouth for comfortable chewing, and spitting out stones that looked as if they had been scraped by a knife.

The doe split an apple, after making three dents in the skin. While she munched on a scliff, with juice bubbles gathering on her chin, Skip snatched the remainder, manœuvring it in his jaws till he had his teeth in the pulp. He cut through, after much head shaking, by squeezing the apple hard against his toothless upper gums. Like Bounce, he still lacked the power to split an intact apple; his baby teeth yielded under the pressure of his jaws. So all three had to wait till the doe prepared the way. Perhaps she understood their weakness, for she took only one bite at each apple, then left it to her fawns.

Bounce ate many slices from apples opened by his mother, then wandered back to the bush where he had found five plums. He found no more on the ground, but discovered he could reach those on the bush by rearing up tall. It was when he was pulling down his second plum that he saw a strange deer approaching—a young doe with plump flanks, about the same age as himself. Bounce moved to greet her, then recoiled at the smell of dog. He stamped with a foot while his flag opened like a flower after rain. For how could he know that the little doe was his sister, bringing dog smell with her because she had just left the bed she shared with her owner's collie bitch?

For the space of a minute brother and sister stared at each other, the doe stretching her neck to query with her nose, Bounce straining back with forelegs braced. The little doe was curious; uncertain but unafraid. *Nee-ee-eep*, she said, pricking her ears. The old doe heard the greeting, and looked up in question. Then she saw, and came over to investigate. And Patrick MacPherson, standing behind the curtained window with the bitch on a chair beside him, witnessed a strange scene in his orchard.

At the approach of the big deer the little doe started to squeal. When the big stranger was standing beside Bounce she cowered belly to earth, with legs spread wide, and squealed. The old doe's ears went up; Bounce cringed back; Skip and Dance came over to see. Patrick frowned in perplexity. The collie growled deep in her throat, because she recognised the cry as well as her master recognised the pose. Twice in the past the fawn had grovelled squealing—once when cornered by a roving dog, and once when threatened by a moocher with a stick.

Patrick laid a restraining hand on the trembling dog. He could let her out of the wondow in a moment if danger threatened the fawn. And he wanted to discover why a little roe doe should be afraid of her own kind. That puzzled Patrick most, for he had always taken it for granted that his foundling would one day go off to the woods to rejoin her clan. Instead, confronted by a mother doe, she was displaying in the way she did to strange dogs or rough men who crowded her too close.

The old doe stepped forward. She, too, recognised cry and posture, though she was at a loss concerning the cause. To identify it with herself was completely beyond her powers. She saw a fawn in acute distress; she could see no likely cause; so her instinctive reaction was to nuzzle her reassuringly. Yet, when she reached down with her muzzle, the fawn crouched still flatter, stabbing the grass with her forehooves and whimpering with ears laid back. Perplexed, but not discouraged, the doe dunted the quivering flanks gently with her muzzle. She uttered soft sounds in her throat; sounds beyond the ability of man to understand. And suddenly the frightened fawn relaxed, struggling to her feet when she felt her ears licked by a warm, comforting tongue.

The old man at the window, thankful he hadn't interfered, was certain the time had come for the fawn to go back to her own. He became still more certain when he saw her follow the herd through the foxgloves and ferns at the orchard hedge, and skip away after them across the open field. Yet, presently, she stopped and looked back. She stood still while the others bounded towards Dry-flatts. Then, suddenly, she was scampering towards home, tossing her head and kicking her heels. Patrick met her in the orchard, and stood fingering his red beard in wonder while she held up her muzzle to be licked by the tongue of his dog.

Morning after morning, in the cool, misty daybreak, the deer visited the orchard, travelling by Stane Farm and the

Wood-of-no-name from their harbour in Glencryan; and each morning they met Patrick MacPherson's fawn, who was taller than little Dance. Sometimes they went there after nightfall; but such visits were fleeting, and the doe soon left for Dryflatts and her feeding grounds beyond. Her usual evening circuit was Dryflatts, Skeoch Farm, Hoolet Nest; then back to Glencryan across the moor. But there were mornings when she went into the Dryflatts larches to lie up for the day, for the wood was her second harbour.

Then one morning, when the sky was misted blue and the fire kindling in the birches, they lingered over-long in the Fin-mc-oot orchard. The little doe left them as usual in the middle of the field, and raced back to her pressed couch under an apple tree. Rabbits, nibbling grass among the rushes, sat up to stare when the herd turned down the field instead of crossing straight to Dryflatts. At the field bottom, beyond an unkempt boundary hedge of thorn and briar, the ground sloped steeply to the burn.

The doe leaped through a gap over strands of barbed wire, then turned to munch scarlet hips, breasting down cow parsnip and angelica, and many-headed thistles, in her eagerness to reach them. The fawns snatched the glistening, waxy fruits from lower twigs, blinking their eyes as they chewed. Bounce, standing hock-deep in hemp nettles, saw black fruits among the red, where bramble tendrils trailed under the spreading briars. Boring through the tangle, he rubbed against burdock with ripe, spiny fruits. When he pulled out a few minutes later he had seven burrs hooked to his flank and sixteen blackberries in his paunch.

Gorse, growing in dense masses on the slope, hid the deer as they filed to the burn. The burnside flat was sandy, hoof-marked, and printed by the feet of a heron

and many rabbits. Beneath the deer's feet the burn ran
bright over tinted pebbles; but the opposite bank was
high and overhung by willows, and there the water flowed
deep. On the sunlit amber bottom, troutlets swirled ooze
clouds as they darted. The doe touched noses with her
own water image, and snorted without drinking. Instead,
she turned round, to lick long and eagerly at a white-
veined stone. On the burnside flat she was fifty yards from
the road and five hundred from Dryflatts, where the
larches were yellowing.

Suddenly, the doe threw up her head, and wheeled to
face the road, with nostrils wide and ears listening forward. When a big lorry appeared, its engine revving
noisily as the driver changed gear for the hill, she had no
thought of fleeing; for she was used to traffic on the road,
and had no reason to panic. But when the lorry stopped
with a squeal of brakes, and a man jumped from the
cabin, her flag opened and closed in uncertainty. Then
a second man appeared, holding a big dog by the collar,
and she was faced with decisions.

The dog was big, lean and smoke coloured, and shaggy
in the coat; he had wolfish jaws, long legs and a wiry
tail; and he was fast, fresh and foxy, with the nose of a
foxhound. That he had killed Bounce's sister was something the doe couldn't know; that he was dangerous she
realised at a glance. So she broke before he was slipped;
and was on the slope among the gorse when he leaped the
roadside fence. Her attitude to dogs was usually one of
confident watchfulness. Greyhounds she feared; but to
collies, or terriers, or retrievers, she seldom yielded ground,
unless they were accompanied by men. In the moocher's
lurcher, Sam, she recognised a serious menace to her
fawns—an antagonist that a mature, antlered buck would
be hard pressed to handle.

Sam made ground at the start by running the edge of

the gorse brake and going up the slope on a slant. When he crashed through the hedge, yelping at the restraining clutch of briars, he was fifty yards behind the deer, out on their left, and barring the route to Dryflatts. Viewing him, the doe kept straight on for Glencryan, with rabbits bolting ahead of her because they knew she ran in fear. The rabbits fanned out along the roadside dyke, seeking crannies among crumbling whin stones. A kestrel, sitting on the dyke top with a fat vole in her claws, flashed out, round, and up to the overhead wires, where she screighed with the prey hanging limply from her beak.

The doe leaped boldly where the dyke-top wires had sagged, thus choosing the route least likely to baulk her fawns. Bounce was in the air before she reached the hedge across the road; then came Dance, open-mouthed; then Skip, who stumbled to his knees. The others were through a gap in the hedge, bounding high and fast across the Stane Farm stubble, before he struggled to his feet. He was barely through the hedge when Sam leaped at the dyke. The lurcher slid on his face at the jump down, burring his pads and grazing a tusk; and the kestrel, shrilling *wree-wree-wree* from the wires, dropped her vole on the verge.

Sam breinged at the hedge, while the kestrel flapped down to retrieve her vole. His slip had lost him ground, and he felt a prickle in his foot; but the yards gained by his fall meant little to Skip, who was now far behind the others and ready to panic. While the doe and two fawns sailed across the stubble in tremendous bounds, Sam bore down on the third, with teeth bared and head skewed, ready for the kill.

Skip heard the thud and crackle of the dog's feet in the stubble and jumped six feet sideways without slackening pace. He was blowing, with lower lip drawn away from his teeth, and his tongue protruding from the side of his mouth. The lurcher shot past, trying to turn short. The fawn gained five yards, which he lost after twenty bounds in the direction of Stane Farm. Again he leaped aside; and again Sam overshot. Twice more he escaped by frantic sideways leaps, fighting gamely for his life, his weakened lungs tortured by the strain. Then Sam was upon him, and he screamed a terrible scream as strong teeth reached for his neck.

At the top of the field, the doe heard the cry—that unutterably poignant cry, so like the voice of a child in acute distress. Turning almost in her stride, she galloped back down the field, leaving Bounce and Dance at the hedgerow ditch to pant new strength into their lungs. Fifty paces from the dog she changed direction, and started to circle; the dog, mouthing the dead fawn without savagery, bared teeth still red with his blood. At that moment the moocher reached the drystane dyke across the road, bawling fresh instructions to the dog. The doe gave an ear to the man, but kept her eyes on Sam, tapping nervously with a foot when she saw him reaching down to sniff her dead fawn.

Then, suddenly, he leaped at her with a thunderous growl; that was the moocher's instruction and he was prompt to obey. Her courage wavering in the presence of the man, the doe plunged away, keeping even distance ahead of the dog and leading him across the field away from her fawns. But Sam soon realised he couldn't catch her; and Sam was wise. So he turned away from her line to cut off the fawns, who were running along the far side of the hedge to keep touch with the doe. Bounce hissed through his nostrils in fear, then turned uphill for Glen-cryan, with Dance bounding in his slots and Sam peril-ously close.

But Sam's change of mind had its effect on the doe.

Now a terrible rage was born in her heart. The pattern was simple; her reaction instinctive, inevitable and as old as time. Skip had died when she thought he was following; dead before she was aware of the threat. But now the issue was plain. She saw her remaining fawns directly threatened; she was their mother; and the enemy was there in plain view. So she bounded away after Sam—not to avenge her dead, but to protect the living. And the moocher, watching, wondered. . . .

Bounce, his white rump plain to the eyes of the man at the road, fled through great clumps of rushes towards the birch swamp on the north flank of Glencryan, with Dance holding her place and the lurcher catching up. Three carrion crows, with earth-soiled beaks, flapped into the air, then swooped at the dog. Sam, snarling without losing pace, pressed closer on the fawns. He was three lengths from Dance when he was aware of the doe at his side. One mighty leap put her ahead; then she turned hard in front of him, running side on, forcing him to check and change direction.

The fawns gained the birches and disappeared in the dense reed thickets. Pigeons, clattering from the oaks, flew out from the wood, then turned away sharply with a flick of blue wings when they saw the dog. Sam, running flank to flank with the deer, was unable to head her, so he leaped to the attack, knowing he had lost the fawns. But the doe, expecting such a move, halted dead in her tracks, and reared up to counter. Sam missed her shoulder, and fell off balance; and in that moment she struck him with a hoof.

The blow took the lurcher on the side of the head. It lifted skin, and drew blood, dazing Sam momentarily and rousing him to terrible fury. But the doe didn't wait for his second assault. Her purpose was achieved. She had fought to protect her fawns, and they were safe; to continue the fight had neither meaning nor purpose. So she fled in the direction of Dryflatts, to shake off the lurcher before going to seek her fawns.

And two hours later she joined them in Glencryan, in the harbour by the oak tree when rain was falling.

9

BOUNCE STARTED SHEDDING HIS SUMMER COAT WHEN the first coloured leaves were shaken from the trees, and the yellow was bright on the larches. When the flower clusters of the bell heather shrivelled he was touzie on the neck, with grey tufts showing through the red. Each time he rubbed his flank against a tree he left red hairs on the bark; and when he shook his head they fell from his neck in a shower.

One morning the Stane Farm swallows flew out and did not return. Rooks thronged the stubbles, where cushats were gathering corn for half-fledged chicks in flimsy nests in the dark spruces of Glencryan. Peewits and redshanks deserted the rushy pastures; fieldfares and redwings came. By day the fireweed gave its goosedown to the wind; and at night the leaves fell steadily under the stars.

The deer nibbled ripe blackberries when the bramble leaves were scarlet, feeding at nightfall and dawn along woodside and hedgerow. The fawns shed their front teeth, and for a week or more cropped no grass. During the toothless days they filled their paunches with berries— bramble and scarlet hip; rowan and haw and elder; and the wersh plums of the sloe. Bounce discovered a liking for the sweet cuplets of the yew; he also ate a little of the foliage. But best of all he liked the glistening hips of the dogrose, which the fieldfares shredded by day. It was when he was seeking hips in the hedgerow tangles that he gathered on the coat the burrs of the burdock, which were rubbed off later, or fell with falling hair. Where they fell, new plants would grow, whose fruits other deer would carry in another year.

The doe found a new harbour deeper in Glencryan, close by the leaning chestnut tree on the south side of the wood. It was a warm thicket of windfalls, bracken and scrub birch, hemmed in by pines. There the deer rested by day when the sun was warm, couching to leeward of the tangles when the wind blew chill among the pines, or the rain was driving from the west.

One morning Bounce was lying under the down-spreading branches of the chestnut, dozing with muzzle turned in against his flank. As he slept, his ears kept watch, moving independently and together. The hair on his neck was matted, like fur that has been soiled and wet, and rubbed the wrong away. On his forehead was a dark patch of hair, in pattern like head of thistle; and from the flat top his first antler buds were sprouting—resilient spikes under soft, dense fur.

He woke when Smoky Joe flapped on to a chestnut bough, and called *Kwarp*. While Bounce licked his neck, getting hair on his tongue, the crow nipped off a barbed, green fruit and dropped it, tilting forward on his perch to watch it fall. Bounce looked up without fear. The crow flew down to catch a wolf spider that was scurrying over the buff and gold carpet of chestnut leaves; he ate it, blinking his grey, inner eyelid, then said *Ha!* and flew away. Bounce, thrusting himself from his knees, sniffed at green, prickly fruits scattered on the ground. Some were split, revealing the brown, smooth nuts under the skin; others lay open and discoloured with the freed fruit beside them. Bounce nosed them, and threatened to butt them with his head; but he made no move to taste. Instead, he danced back with a toss of his head, which loosened more fine hairs from his neck.

Out on the moor the birches flamed in the sunfire. Cloud shadows raced across the heather where grouse were calling. High up, an arrowhead of quacking mallard sped swiftly across the cloud-race to circle in a blue space of sky before dropping down to the loch. Bounce rubbed ear against shoulder and sauntered through browning heath rushes and shrivelled bog asphodel towards a gully hidden by massed, silver-barked birches. In the gully, under the birch screen, peaty water trickled over cool, mossed stones.

He sucked water thirstily under a cloud of flies, then turned away, drooling. With his new teeth he bit off a yellow birch leaf, which he dropped without chewing. On his way back, he stopped by a dub of green-scummed water; there was a grass clump in the middle, and on it were two white eggs. The eggs had been put there by John Long, the keeper, and when the crows ate one he replaced it with another, treated so that crows which sucked would never suck again. Many black crows died with clenched feet after tasting white eggs; but the keeper failed to take Smoky Joe, who was the greatest egg eater of them all.

Bounce returned to the thicket to find Dance lying down, scratching an ear with a hindfoot; but of his mother he could see no sign. The little doe rose to greet him, dunting him on the shoulder with her head, and together they butted at the lichened, curling bark of a fallen, hollow tree, in which tits had nested when the roots were in the ground. Bounce rubbed off shreds and flinders with his velveted antler buds, uncovering spiders which darted to new crannies. When he stepped back with his sister two blue tits whisked down to probe for the spiders.

Presently he saw his mother returning through the pines. With her came an antlered buck, grizzled of face, his neck patchy with the moult. Perhaps Bounce recognised him; certainly he showed no fear. And when he loped over to sniff the stranger's muzzle he was graciously allowed to sniff.

The buck, now only five inches taller than Bounce, had come to rejoin his family, after running solitary since the rut. That day all four lay up in the thicket, sleeping and chewing cud. Once, midway through the afternoon, when the blackcock were in the birches pecking at buds, Bounce struggled to his feet and prodded playfully at the doe's moulting neck. Getting no response, he presented his head to the buck, who stabbed at him sideways without force or anger. The buck was a switch-horn, uncommon among roe; his antlers were straight and sharp, with no prongs in front and unforked behind—the deadliest weapons a roebuck could carry. But with Bounce he was gentle; and when he pushed the fawn away there was no glitter in his eyes.

An upcurled branch attracted his attention after the buck turned cheek to flank to show he wanted to sleep. It grew from the base of the hollow tree, and ended in a fork like the antlers of a roe. Whether he was attracted by the resemblance, or whether the height just suited him, is hard to say; but he pranced up to it, head askew, and engaged it with a sideways thrust. Rearing when it yielded, he drew away two paces, stamped his foot, then went in head down. With his forehead in the cleft he butted and bored and stabbed, dancing in a half-circle and furrowing the loam with his hooves. Once he straddled the prostrate trunk in his efforts to force the branch down. A stroke of his sharp right hoof sliced off mossed, spongy bark, uncovering a ladybird beetle and the dried legs and wings of flies. He gave up at last when he felt Dance prodding his flag. By then there was a single drop of blood on the tip of one furred antler bud.

Wind-blown rain hid the sun at its setting, and silence closed down with the brooding mists. When the deer went to drink they had a web of moisture on the brittle hair of their backs, and their knees were dark from contact with the earth. They could hear One Eye *wicking* plaintively on his pine roost, for the owl couldn't, or wouldn't, hunt in drifting mists or rain. Then, suddenly, the wet mists rifted; the sky cleared; and a thin crescent of moon rose pale among the stars. One Eye hooted, a long drawn out bubbling cry; and, presently, Bounce saw him wafting from the pines, scanning the ground for mice.

The deer gathered hips along the woodside, moving as they fed. There rabbits were feeding, their white fuds flashing as they ambled through the wet moor grass. Musk smell came to the nostrils of Bounce when he was pulling hips, with his forefeet on a rock. When a stoat poked its triangular head from a crevice, he struck out instantly with his forefeet, for stoat hatred was born with the old wound on his neck, and he now treated them all as foxes treat cats. Thus the roe of olden days looked upon the martens of the hills, which were slayers of their kids. But the stoat had not the remotest idea of harrying a roe, however young; he was interested in the rabbits grazing in the open. So he tissed and launched musk smell, and darted hurriedly under the briar.

Bounce lay down among clumps of mat grass when his paunch was full, and touched noses with Dance when she came to rest beside him. A little distance away, the doe was trotting in circles with the buck, who kept putting his chin on her neck and touching her shoulder with his forehooves. They gave up their love-game when a big badger shambled from the wood. Brock ignored the deer; he was there to hunt the tussocks, hoping to find a rabbit in a snare. He had found two on other nights, and eaten his fill on the spot; and the theft was blamed on foxes, because the moocher didn't know there were badgers in Glencryan. Had he known he might have guessed why part of the rabbits was left; for the badger, unlike the fox, doesn't carry food home.

Brock, finding no rabbits, returned to the wood. The fawns, being curious, followed him a little way, and saw him climb the rock on which Bounce had stood. They watched him eating dog hips, till he could reach no more. When he climbed down, and entered the wood, they could still see him among the trees, for his striped face was plain in the half-light of the crescent moon.

The fawns played and rested during most of the night. When the daybreak was near, they were still on the fringe of Glencryan; the buck was too concerned with the doe to wander far from his harbour. Daylight came with a chirp of frost in the grass, and grey geese filling the sky with their music as they flew overhead in the direction of the loch after their long flight from the north. Pheasants were feeding on the Stane stubbles before the deer loped into the wood, with the fawns leading the way along the main runway to the thicket among the pines.

At intervals during the day, the buck licked the face of the doe, and danced around her, with his chin on her neck or rump. For almost a week afterwards he harassed her with his attention, rearing, prancing, butting her playfully, or running with her in circles and figures of eight. Yet during it all he neither barked nor postured, nor challenged any passing bⅰck; amorous he was, but in his blood there was no rutting fire. That was now for the red stags of the mountains, swollen of neck, and maned like lions, who filled the corries with their thunder.

Men say this second wooing of the roe has no significance; that the matings come to naught. Yet Nature is not given to meaningless amours, or to matings that have no purpose. The rut that ends when the corn is ripe means fawns at the end of May; but whence come the July fawns, of which there is a goodly number?

All day the leaves drifted down—yellow and brown and red; crimson and flaming scarlet—and at night were driven before the wind. The fire died in the birches. When the sun shone, the rowan-berries were like new blood spattered on the grass; and the larches had a lilac haze that hid their nakedness. Frost, slight without hoar, hanselled the pale rose and silver of the gusty dawns; but no ice sheeted the water of ditch or pond. The burns ran full and clear, carrying their harvest of tinted leaves to the river. And there was no more bird-song; save for the ghost trill of a robin when the mid-morning sky was blue, or the pealing of tiny bells where tits flittered in the trees.

Bounce was playing the forked stick game when the badger came to the thicket. In the shadowy daybreak his black-and-white face was conspicuous; plain as a rabbit's fud or the winter flag of the roe. *Stay away*, it warned; *molest me at your peril!* For Brock feared nothing that roamed the woods, and was powerful in himself; and because he sought quarrel with none, his identity was written on his face.

With the purposeful steps of a beast that knows where he is going, he brushed past Bounce, without grunt or grimace, and fell on the rotting, hollow trunk with his claws. While the fawn stood by, wagging his ears in wonder, Brock clawed away bark, and moss, and lichen, and sent the wood dust flying in clouds. He tore out flies, and spiders, and beetles that kicked feebly on their backs when they fell, without pausing to lick them into his mouth. When he had the trunk waisted like a tree where a beaver has bitten, he sniffed at the porous wood, turned his little pig-eyes on the fawn, and grunted. Then he renewed his attack on the trunk in excited fury.

Presently the log sagged, exposing a hollow edged with brown and silver splinters, and a fat hedgehog coiled in sleep. The badger poked him out with a black-clawed foot. Bounce shied away, startled, when the ball hit the ground, gathering leaves on the barbs. A thin scream from the hedgehog sent him bounding away in fear; so he didn't see Brock tear the sleeper apart before eating him right down to the quills.

That night the dusk was chill with settling frost. The deer grazed clover in the Stane Farm foggage, where dairy cows trampled for two hours in the brightness of the day; and when the night sky was dark blue, like a rook's wing in sunlight, they rested in the Wood-of-no-name. At midnight, with the moon full and Orion flashing icy fire in a nirly wind, the buck rose and led the way to the hedge, where they browsed lightly on thorn and elder and briar, sniffing critically and biting only at the choicest twigs. Bounce, feeding close to the doe, tried to nose under her flank, but she pushed him off brusquely and turned to face him with her head held low. When he butted her on the forehead with his furred, two-inch antlers, she played with him not ungently; when he reached up to smell her muzzle she licked his big ears with her warm tongue; but as soon as he tried to nose under her she danced away, threatening him with her head.

So Bounce returned to his browsing, moving with much crackling through frush raspberry canes that grew thick along the hedgeside ditch. The hogweed stems, hollow and brittle, snapped when he breasted them down. Once, he butted one, and shook the dry, seeding umbel aloft on his dags. Then he was joined by Dance, and together they sniffed at flaky paper fragments, curled and scalloped, that were strewn under the exposed, knuckle root of a thorn. While they were sniffing, a woodmouse whisked out and away, startling them mightily and scurrying down the hedgebottom with a noise like leaves swirling in the wind.

They were lying side by side, chewing cud among the dry raspberry canes, when the woodmouse came back. She peered at them for a moment with her jet, boot-button eyes, then vanished under the thorn root with a big haw in her teeth. Inside the burrow was an eight-tier wasp nest, still intact; but now the hexagonal grub cells were empty, and only a few shrivelled wasps, clasping legs to faces in death, remained. The guardian legions, who had tended the grubs so selflessly in the citadel's sunny heyday, had slain them with terrible ruthlessness at the first leaf-fall, then scattered in the misted sun-glare to gorge on heady jam and overripe fruit and die on bending flower heads in a blaze of glory. And the woodmouse had taken the citadel, and pulled down the wasp-made paper shell, and made herself a warm nest and a store for her berries and stubble grain. And all that remained of the once powerful colony was the year's young queens, asleep in dyke crannies or under the curled bark of sycamores, with the wasp millions of the future in their loins.

Yet again, while daylight was still far off, the deer rose to feed. Ignoring the woodside hedge, they filed slowly to the road, with the switch-horn buck in the lead. All four walked with their ears up and their heads high. When the buck leaped out on to the road at the broken gate the doe did not follow at once; she lingered to wag her ears, to test the side-wind, and rub her neck against a post. The buck was halfway down the slope, making fire-crackle noises on frosted leaves and twigs, before she stepped on to the moonlit road with her fawns at foot.

On the slope above the burn they browsed on twigs of down-spreading beech branches, without haste or eagerness, while rabbit feet rustled among brushwood and pattered on the frosted leaf carpet. The deer heard, without hearkening; they could interpret rabbit tread, and knew when to ignore and when to throw up heads in question. Near Bounce a white rabbit was scraping in the mould to uncover bluebell bulbs untouched by frost. It was the only white rabbit in the neighbourhood, having failed to give birth to one young of abnormal colour in three litters reared under the same tree root on the slope.

Bounce had his head down, and a half notion of butting the rabbit, when One Eye flew into the wood, making the glen ring with his *wicking*. The white rabbit fled, spurning mould and dead leaves, and the footfalls of the others were stilled. Buck and doe looked up, querying flight and silence, got their answer from the owl, and went on with their browsing. Bounce, unable to see the owl because he looked about instead of up, watched its moon shadow wavering on the ground before it flashed up a gleaming beech trunk to meet One Eye as he pitched. One Eye mewed, and wailed *Kee-wick; kee-wick; kee-wick*, lingering on the first note and clipping the second, so changing his wild, war-cry—by a change of emphasis—to a plaint of hunger and frustration.

For One Eye was hungry. He had hunted from sunset till two hours before midnight, flapping on slow, noiseless wings on the outskirts of Glencryan and watching from corn stacks in the Stane Farm stackyard. During the darkest hours he had roosted in a tree by the cartshed gable, moping and mute. He was in the air again before the deer had left the Wood-of-no-name, hunting in clear moonlight above stubbles and hedgerows, flying front-heavy and silent less than twenty feet above his own ground shadow; but again he had failed to find long-tailed mouse or short-tailed vole to clutch in his foot. So he had flown in to rest before hunting the burn, where water voles nibbled when the moon was high.

Dance and Bounce were lying flank to flank beside a lone holly scrogg when One Eye hooted—a wild, bubbling cry that echoed far through the moonlit trees. From the holly came a subdued flicker of wings, followed by a low, startled *pink*: then silence. The fawns heard, without understanding, and listened for repetition; but One Eye, hearing and understanding with his shrewdly sensitive ears, wafted from his perch and swooped towards the bush.

The fawns jumped up when the owl passed overhead. They ran six paces, then stopped in their slots. Buck and doe minced down to see what was afoot, halting with necks stretched when they were twelve feet from the holly. While four deer watched, prick-eared, One Eye clung flapping to the outermost leaves of the bush, yelping in undertones as he tried to beat his quarry from the cover. Each time he yelped, his breath came in little puffs of vapour from his open beak.

The blackbird in the holly, though secure against attack, was stampeded by the closeness of the owl. So he burst out, pinking in fear, and trailed across the open, with tail spread and wings drooping, towards the low, close cover of a great thicket of rhododendrons. But One Eye, swooping from the bush, clutched him ere he could dart under the first drooping branch. The deer watched the owl flapping to keep balance on his prey, and heard the clatter of his downy wings against the tough, glistening leaves. Bounce stared, with both ears forward, while the buck lowered his head and the doe stamped with a foot. Then One Eye was up and away, leaving on the ground a ring of black feathers, spattered with scarlet, for the foxes to sniff at and drool over. Beside them lay one downy feather, plucked by the blackbird from the breast of the owl when its slim talons clenched in death.

At peep of day the cranreuch was heavy, and the frost smoke trailed on the water. The deer drank under white alders, and were swallowed in the mist when they crossed the burn. On the bank, every grass blade and umbel and withered stem was rimed.

The deer entered the Fin-me-oot orchard as grey geese passed over, airting southwards, high above the smoor, baying like hounds on a line. Small birds were feeding at a bird table among the apple trees—blue tit and coal tit, robin, wren and greenfinch. On the ground a dunnock was searching for the spilled-over crumbs. Bounce reared beside the bird table, frightening away the birds, who flew twittering to rimed twigs to watch him. With his forehooves on the edge of the table, he sniffed and snorted, inhaling enticing smells and blowing away crumbs in clouds of vapour. He ate brown bread and white, six shelled peanuts, and a small piece of fish, before he jumped away, licking his lips.

The others were nibbling on thorn and apple twigs, lipping them many times to clean them of rime before taking in the bite. Bounce pulled at a forked twig, rolled it out with his tongue, and fought with it, bringing down the frost powder in a fine, chill spray. He was shaking the rime from his face when a hen blackbird scurried past his feet in a crouching run. She stopped, with uptilted tail, under a gnurly crab apple, and pecked at a thin box-wood lid lying on the grass. She was pulling, and pushing, with her beak, trying to flick it over, when Bounce danced up to her, with head lowered in playful challenge. But the lid was frozen to the grass, and she was unable to move it. Many times in the past she had turned the lid over, knowing she would find woodlice, and earthworms, and shiny black beetles lurking on the pale, pressed grass underneath. Not till Bounce, reaching down, tried to prod her with his antlers did she flutter away, *peeting* her disappointment. When she was leaf-turning in the hedge-bottom Bounce dislodged the lid with his nose, and tossed it two feet. Then he pulled up, and ate, the stringy, yellow grass it had shielded from the frost.

Rabbits were ambling into the orchard when the deer filed out by a gap in the hedge. That morning there were waxwings in the briars. Without hesitation, the buck cut straight across the misty pasture, instead of turning right for Glencryan. On the road they were startled by a milk lorry, grinding slowly uphill on its way to Stane Farm, and bolted two hundred yards off their line before turning again in the direction of Dryflatts. They crossed the Dryflatts Farm potato field, with its network of iced wheel ruts, and entered the wood through the northside birches, reaching the thick spruce cover as the cushats were flying from their roosts. And when the pheasants were in the field, searching the shaw-strewn ground for chat potatoes, they were snugly harboured in the tangy spruce gloom, wagging ears and chewing cud.

10

THREE WEEKS FROM THE YEAR'S END THE SWITCH-horn buck cast his antlers in Dryflatts—one in a heather clearing, under the big pylon carrying high tension cables; the other under a dense spruce which was a roosting place of Tufter, the long-eared owl.

Bounce was chewing cud under a wind blown spruce when he saw the buck approaching Tufter's tree. The switch-horn was still wearing his off-side antler, having dropped the other under the pylon the previous morning. In its place he had a raw, red sore on which cracked skin was forming. Tufter, drawn up long against the spruce trunk with feather tufts erect, opened his orange eyes wide when the buck reached his tree, then turned to stare at Bounce who had risen to follow. While the switch-horn buck rubbed his antler against one side of the dusty spruce trunk, Bounce pushed with his fore-head against the other, dancing in a half circle with fore-legs bent. Tufter, losing interest, blinked, winked, and closed his eyes in sleep.

For perhaps a minute afterwards the buck continued rubbing—not vigorously, but gently, like a cat easing an itching ear. Then, suddenly, he swung away, pivoting on his hindfeet, and trotted through withered bracken tangles and brushwood to another dark spruce with many cushat feathers clinging to its branches.

The spruce was a tall tree, with sooty, moss-furred trunk, and so heavily foliaged that it could have roosted and hidden a score of pheasants. In the dank, balsamy gloom under the tree lay two fledged cushat squeakers, dead and stiff-legged, with golden hair still clinging to nape and crown. Late hatched, and growing slowly, they had been deserted by their parents ere they were able to fly. In their restlessness, born of two days' hunger, they had shouldered and jostled each other out of the nest. They had been dead three days when the switch-horn's antler toppled and fell beside them.

At first, the buck seemed unaware that anything had happened, for he stood staring through the spruce screen while bloody froth and bubbles formed round the scar on his skull, and a thread of scarlet curled and clotted on the hair above his eyes. Then he shook his head, tongued the inside of a foreleg, sniffed at the shed antler. . . . Bounce, trotting up, smelt it, tapped it with a hoof. . . . The doe, arriving with Dance, picked up the antler, chewed on it tentatively, dropped it, then sniffed at the bloody patch on the buck's skull. Presently, they walked away—the doe returning with Dance to their lie among brashings and touzie bracken, the buck to his favourite lair among scrub birch in a hollow. Bounce scraped a bed on the needle carpet under Tufter's tree, and lay down to chew cud. Beside him were thirty-six castings regurgitated by the owl—mouse-size objects composed of the bones, fur and teeth of rodents, and the feathers of birds—some black, and firm and new, and many bleached and frayed that were old.

After nightfall, when the deer were feeding in the misty pasture, the buck's cast antler was carried away by a big, white-tipped vixen who had just moved into Dryflatts for the winter. Before carrying away the antler, she ate the cushat squeakers on the spot, devouring both at once because she was big and hungry and they were lean and little.

Daybreak came soft and clammy, with the trees

drenched by the mists. In the middle of the forenoon, with the sun limned silver in the haar, the roe were lying among the deep heather on the south side of the wood, wet and steaming, their paunches filled with furze browse, briar twigs and ivy. They had also eaten some hay, which they found at the pasture gate, where it had been put down for outwintering cattle beasts from Dry-flatts Farm. They were awaiting the sun, to bask for an hour before returning to the wood, for on such mornings they sought its warmth as much as they avoided it in summer, so long as they could do so under cover.

All four were now wearing winter garb, which they had completed more than a fortnight before the buck shed his antlers. Their coats were now grey, with long, brittle hair; their flags large and white and softly furred; their faces darker and more grizzled than in summer. On their necks they had twin patches of white—one of half-moon shape on their throats, and another, rectangular, halfway down their gullets. The buck's flashes were whiter than the doe's and the fawns' were whitey-grey. Alone among them the doe had grown two down-pointing hair tufts on her flag, which gave her the appearance of having a tail.

The sun broke through, and its light glanced bright on every twig and thorn. The birches glinted bronze and silver, and water drops sparkled on the heather. Bounce lay on his side, with legs outstretched, taking comfort from the warmth. Every now and again he raised his head, to shake the water-itch from his ears. Then suddenly, when he was passing a forehoof gently between his antler spikes, he was aware of his mother sitting up, neck stretched, ears forward and eyes unwinking. And, in a moment, he heard, and smelt, and saw. . . .

Climbing the roadside fence, beyond the gleaming pylon, were two men with guns. Behind them jumped three dogs—two tan-and-white spaniels and a great,

big-boned Labrador with a coat like a blackcock and a
tail like an otter. Bounce heard them on the road, and
when the fence creaked under their weight; he got their
scent when they crossed into the wind, which was slight
and wayward; and he saw them as they strode through
the heather, with the black dog at heel and the spaniels
questing ahead. So he tensed for a break, watching his
mother for decisions.

But the doe made no move to rise. She was watching
the buck, who was wise and cunning. Many times he had
lain close in cover when men were driving woods, breaking away only when sprung from his lie by a dog; and
many times men had trampled about his ears in a thicket
without suspecting that a deer lay anywhere near. So the
buck stayed down, keeping touch with ears and nose,
prepared to lie close before the questing dogs but ready to
spring if they found him. And the doe, unlike the hind of
the red deer, who leads even when being driven by a
stag, was prepared to trust to his judgement.

Moss cheepers and coal heads fluttered over the heather,
disturbed by spaniels questing on the line of a hare. Two
shots rocked the air when the hare burst from her form,
and the echoes rumbled in Dryflatts. While the hare
screamed, and dragged herself through the heather with
both hind legs shattered, a cock pheasant rose under
the noses of the dogs. The rattle-tinkle of his wings was
heard by the men, and a third shot crumpled him before
he topped the trees. Killed clean, he crashed into the
heather twenty yards from the deer, while his rump
plumes drifted where gunsmoke trailed among blue
spruce needles.

The buck quivered, twitching his nostrils, when the
Labrador came breinging across the heather to retrieve
the kill. Bounce tensed for a leap that would take him up
and away without going through the ritual of rising from

his knees. He heard the snuffling of the dog, the rustle of its feet in the heather, and its sudden intake of breath when it found the bird: then it was crashing back to its master, with head high, tail gay, and the pheasant secure in its jaws. Men's voices came to his ears for some time afterwards, and the strong scent of dogs to his nose; but the tension was gone from him and he had no urge to panic. So he learned, by example, the old roe trick of lying close in cover. And when the men, having smoked, at last left the pylon and disappeared among the trees, he went over to sniff long and curiously, and eat the cigarette ends they had dropped in the heather.

That winter the deer used three harbours. On windless mornings, when the mists were rosy in the sunrise, they couched in a ferny hollow on the moor, under high peat banks crowned with heather, where the sun came warm at noon. There grouse flocked to eat grit, and drink from the narrow water channel that flowed bright over pebbles and green, mossed stones. In the hollow were many bleached bones and soiled wisps of feathers, the remains of ducklings and grouse chicks and song-birds which Smoky Joe had washed before eating, dabbling them in the water with his beak till they were limp and sodden. Each sunset, when the grouse had been feeding on heather for an hour, the roe left the hollow after drinking, and did not return in the night. They took their night rest where they grazed, or on the fringe of Glencryan, seeking their sunning hollow in the morning if they sensed no weather change.

When the dawns came dark and blustering, with driving rain or sleet, or drifting mists, or snell winds threatening snow, they sought the damp, sheltering gloom of the Dryflatts spruces, or thickets in the birch of Glencryan, where they rested by day. On nights of moonlight or darkness, starlight or smirring rain, they foraged afield, travelling far on well-worn runways and trailless byways, yet seldom venturing more than a mile from their harbour in any direction. But when the nights were storm-shaken, with the gale soughing in the trees and the high-tension cables crackling and sizzling in sheeted rain or sleet, they browsed along the wood-edge under cover. And, on such nights, Tufter huddled on his roost, hungry and voiceless, while One Eye wailed his plaint till daylight in Glencryan.

Foxes started calling when the moon was high, travelling many miles each night on tireless pads with the mating fever upon them. Bounce smelt them on the wind and saw their eyes, like aizles, in the dark. The deer paid heed to any fox running near, unafraid but alert for fox-tricks, which they discouraged by stamping and lowering their heads. The Dryflatts vixen they treated with cool indifference, for she kept out of their way and did not trespass on their daytime privacy. Then one morning, while the grey geese were flighting from the loch, in swift arrow flight under racing clouds, the Dryflatts truce was broken. . . .

Bounce, dawdling behind the herd on the wheatfield end-rigg, lingered at a hollow hidden by birches and thorns within gunshot of the wood. The hollow was used as a dumping place for tins and empty bottles by John Long and Dryflatts Farm. A tin marked SYRUP attracted Bounce by its smell, so he stumbled in to reach it, unaware of the menace of ragged, broken bottles that had once severed an artery in the foot of a fox. With the lidless syrup tin in his mouth he stepped back hastily, holding his head to one side while he licked the sweet dregs with his tongue. Becoming angry because he couldn't reach the bottom, where the main sweetness lay, he laid down the tin and thrust in his muzzle, pushing forcefully with his head till the skin of his face was bulging over the rim.

And when his tongue at last reached bottom he went down on his knees and butted as he licked.

It was after he had cleaned the tin, and tapped it from his muzzle with a forehoof, that he realised the herd had gone to harbour without him. He trotted through the birches, licking nose and chin sticky with syrup, and entered the wood beside a big ash tree in which many fieldfares were roosting, all facing one way. On the main runway he slowed to a walk, undeterred by fox smell blown to him from a thicket by a stray whidder of wind. Even when the white-tipped vixen appeared suddenly in front of him, with slitted eyes and lips curling over tusks, he minced slowly forward, threatening her with three-inch antlers still in velvet. Inch by inch she retreated, with rump arched, brush down and teeth bared to the gums. Then, without warning, she leaped for his throat. And, in that same moment, Bounce was assaulted by a second fox, attacking from behind.

The second fox was the white-tipped vixen's mate—a powerful, grey moor fox, with much-scarred mask, who had already killed lambs and spotted roe fawns. In five years of hard living he had never forced conclusions with a sapling buck; but now, with a partner of the same fibre as himself, he had connived at co-operation and ambush.

Bounce jumped backwards, then sideways, on stiff legs with flag spread, foiling the vixen leaping at his throat and eluding her partner's spring at his neck. The dog fox, following through after missing, chopped the fawn's withers as he landed, then was hurled almost on top of his mate. Stung by the wound, Bounce leaped vertically, and lashed out with a hindfoot. His hoof struck the dog fox on the mouth, splitting his lip clean through and breaking his left tusk at the gum. With a yelp he recoiled, while Bounce, lowering his head at the touchdown, butted the vixen's front teeth with his prongs.

At that moment the buck and doe came crashing through the brushwood. Pigeons clattered from the trees and the fieldfares in the ash tree fled. The dog fox, his mouth dripping blood, flattened his ears and fled. For one crazy moment the vixen lingered to flash ivory at the doe; then she, too, snaked off, belly to earth, escaping by a miracle from the buck's pounding hooves. Wide-eyed and panting, Bounce bounded to his mother's side, to be caressed by her understanding muzzle. In the heat of battle he had found fire and anger and a reckless courage; now he was timorous and shaken, with no feelings of elation—a brave little boy in need of mothering. And the doe mothered him tenderly, nuzzling his cut withers and scuffed antler prongs, before returning to her couch among the spruces.

Throughout the following week, with larks singing and the sun clear in a white-flecked sky, the deer lay up in the fern brake on the moor. Ice filmed the water channel, but in the windless days the old year's dead bracken was warm. At noon, midges danced in clouds under the birches, where blackcock had gathered to feed on catkins at dawn; and during the long nights of frost and star glitter One Eye hooted and wooed in Glencryan.

Other deer came to feed on the moor edge at dusk and dawn—a slim doe and her fawn, accompanied by a tall buck with the scar of an old bullet wound on his neck. During the darkness the herds mixed freely, the three fawns grazing and running together, and resting beside either doe when chewing cud. The old does were casually friendly, feeding close and lying near each other without demonstration. But the bucks were less sociable, threatening and skirmishing, or rearing to box vigorously with their forehooves. Sometimes they circled head to head, but they were wary during the engagements, for their half-grown antlers were still in velvet.

Paired partridges were running in the hedgebottoms, calling *Ka-ar-wit: ka-ar-wit*, when the winter's first snow swirled from the east. The first flakes settled, unmelting, because the iron was on the ground, and at nightfall it was two inches deep in the pastures. When the sky cleared the moon's icy talon was high among the stars, and the snow crunched under the hooves of the roe when they went out to feed.

At first they nibbled heather shoots, which were not a favourite food, because the grass was sealed away and the trees rimed and crusted with snow. But at midnight, in a nirling east wind that iced the buds and feathered the farmhouse windows, they trekked to the gate of the Dry-flatts pasture where the breath of cattle was a vapour cloud on the air. Nine beasts standing meekly with backs to the wind ignored the deer; but the tenth, a rigwoodie bullock caked to the knees with frozen glaur, hustled them from the scattered hay. So the deer fed running in circles, snatching rips of hay when the bullock was away from the gate of slung poles, and bounding clear, chewing, when he shambled up to threaten.

Four hours from daybreak more snow fell, whirling in the wind. It blotted out moon and stars, and filled the slots of the deer in the field. When the sky cleared for the second time that morning, the snow lay level on the Stane Farm furrows.

The buck rose, after chewing cud in the lee of the pasture hedge, and led the herd across the fields towards the Wood-of-no-name. The new snow was fetlock deep on the crust of the old. On the wood edge they met Brock, who had been abroad since twilight. The badger had blood smears on his face and most of a rabbit in his belly. Between the snowfalls he had fought two foxes who had found the rabbit in a snare, nipping them in the pads and getting their hair in his teeth. The deer crossed his incoming tracks in the glen; his outgoing presses were buried under the second snow.

One Eye was wicking in a tree when the herd crossed the burn, having just lost a water vole which had jinked on his blind side and eluded his claws. Along the burnside the alders and birches were rimed, and icicles hung where in summer the leaves of woodrush drooped. The buck followed the burn to the bridge where it flowed under the main north road, then turned along the fence till he found a break. With the doe and fawns running in his slots, he passed along the village street, between dark-walled houses with white roofs and unlit, frosted windows. At the cross-roads he forked right, slotting snow yet unmarked by boot or tyre.

Three shaggy horses were snorting at the gate opposite Thirteen Beeches when the deer leaped into the field through a wired gap in the hedge. The buck took his herd up the field at a gallop, followed by three heavy-hoofed horses with manes and tails flying. A hare, nibbling among splayed, broken rushes, nibbled on unstartled by the thudding hooves. The deer left the horses at the first thorn hedge, and followed a stone-strewn cart track to the road at Heatherfield. They were crossing to the birch roundel when the bullet-scarred buck, with his doe and fawn, reached the road a mile from the village, at a point where two yearling roe had already been killed by lorries since the turn of the year.

In the roundel a second season buck was harbouring alone. He was lean and fluked, and in process of growing a second forward prong on his antlers. Uninvited, he joined the herd, and followed them into the warm thickets of Cowther. At first, he was inclined to be rough with Bounce, who butted him roughly in return; but when the doe dunted him on the ribs with her head he accepted the warning without rancour, and contented himself with prodding at sticks and imaginary fawns.

While the snow lay and the ice thickened, the herd spent the days in Cowther. They were days of heatless sun and blue skies, with rooks dibbling in the hard snow and cushats flocking into garden and stackyard to feed on kale and corn in the mornings. In the midday sun bats wavered out from the web-tangled stable rafters to hawk above the snow on the south side of the wood. The snow shrunk slowly in the daytime thaw, and at night was glassed in the frost.

One morning the buck disappeared with the two-year-old when the herd were feeding in the haugh between the Heatherfield ridge-end and Cowther. At sunrise they had not returned. Doe and fawns left the haugh without seeking them, and followed the burn till they reached a low-lying pond, fed by field drains and the overflow from spates. A mallard duck and drake were standing, hunch-shouldered, on the verge, hungry after gleaning in the Cowther stackyard. The pond ice was wet in the morning thaw. On its surface a stickleback was flapping and wriggling. Bounce licked ice water, and ice, before running after the doe. By then the stickleback had flapped itself to death, unnoticed by the mallards because their eyes were closed.

Late that afternoon the Cowther Farm terrier was hunting rabbits in the wood. The roe lay close in their thicket, keeping track of her with their ears. Bounce, couched a little distance from the others, on a dry leaf carpet under a low-spreading beech, was licking a foreleg when he heard the bitch approaching. Realising that she was coming straight for his lie, he jumped up to face her with chin tucked in and antlers forward. Suddenly, she appeared from the undergrowth, sandy-hued with black muzzle, wire-haired and rabbit-size, running fast on short legs, and barking as she came.

Bounce stamped as she swerved, and shook his head when she faced him. Then he leaped forward, to take her with his head. The thrust was lightning swift, but the bitch was no longer there. She was six feet away, back-tracking slowly, with ears and wire tail down, barking as she retreated. She was barking to hide her own nervous-ness and uncertainty, being a yearling with little experi-ence, and not naturally savage. She had killed rats, but had still to see the inside of her first fox earth. When Bounce rushed at her a second time, she ran behind the beech trunk and sat down to peer at him, with head cocked and tail sweeping leaves.

The moment she stopped barking Bounce's attitude changed. He reached out to sniff her, then turned away, rubbing his ear against the inside of his knee. He lay down, and started to chew cud, watching her with his big, luminous eyes. Presently she came sidling towards him, grimacing, lifting her ears, and twitching her tail between her hocks. Bounce sat still, head up, chewing. And, sud-denly, she was sniffing his neck and ears, licking his muzzle with a long, pink tongue, and dancing on her hind legs pawing playfully at his dags. So they played for many minutes—the farm terrier and a wild roe near his twelvemonth—and when she left at last, after much fussing, he followed her a little distance through the wood.

Five days later the buck came back, without the two-year-old, and the herd returned to Glencryan, travelling in bright moonlight by Heatherfield and Thirteen Beeches to the bridge, and browsing in the glen to the Fin-me-oot orchard. In the raw, gusty dawn they entered the wood, where the last of the snow lay shrunken and discoloured in sunless hollows and along the northside fence.

THE APRIL DAWNS CAME GREY WITH SMIRRING RAIN
when the blackcock danced their rigadoon on the
lekking ground in Glencryan. Curlews, like witches in wet
feathers, flew calling in the soft, moonless dark, and their
wild coronach was carried far by the wind. And on the
loch there was no more goose-talk, for grey lag and white-
front, in disciplined array, had flown north with the wintering duck to the Baltic and Greenland and Novaya
Zemlya, and the bleak Arctic lands that had seen their birth.

One Eye was carrying voles to his mate and three white
owlets before the swallows arrived in the cloudy daybreak,
on wet wings tired after their long flight from Africa. The
roe, nibbling aspen leaves and young shoots of snakeweed
in the Stane Farm lane, saw the birds on roof-ridge and
overhead wires, and sipping water from the duckpond on
the wing. Ten birds were perched on the wires, twittering
and running beaks through feathers, when the deer passed
by on their way to the wood. Many more were flying
towards the North Star, to seek their summer homes
among the cobwebs and oat dust and paraffin smoke, the
bark and moo and quack and cock-a-doodle-doo of the
remotest farms and steadings.

That morning Bounce was restless, shaking his head
and rubbing his prongs against Dance's unwilling legs. At
the base of his antlers the coronets had grown—great
burred rings of bone pressing out against the skin and
strangling the supply of blood to the velvet. So he wanted
to soothe the strange irritation by rubbing, as he did

with a rain-itching ear. But Dance, tiring of having her slim legs used as a rubbing post, defeated him in the end by lying down beside her mother. For perhaps half an hour he prowled about the thicket, poking into brushwood heaps and scraping his antler-dirks against rotten birch poles from which the bark was curling; then, when the cushats were croodling in the clouded sunrise, he bounded over a windfall and disappeared among the trees.

In Braeburn Strip, where many trees were holed by the beaks of woodpeckers, he found a solitary harbour among young larch trees in a mouldy hollow. The larches were nine feet high, surrounded by broken, rusted netting that had kept out rabbits when the trees were planted. In one of them a shilfa was building her nest of hazelraw and horsehair and soft green moss. She flew *twinking* to the leader shoot when the buck started rubbing against the stem of the larch, and fluttered nervously from twig to twig as he wrecked her fragile nest with tormenting antlers.

When Bounce lay down to rest, the velvet on his antlers was scuffed and cut, and the larch stem was frayed by his rubbing. He spent the day in the planting, resting and chewing cud, rising four times to scrape larch stems and thrash the lower branches with his dags. At sunset he left to join the herd in Glencryan, approaching the wood on a slant to keep the wind on his face. A woodcock was flying round the beeches, calling *croak-croak-chissick; croak-croak-chissick*, roding above his mate who was sitting on four eggs among brushwood on the ground leaf carpet. The hen *chissicked* as Bounce approached, and the cock dropped beside her, and presently they were chasing each other in bat-flight at roe height among the flushed beech boles.

On the moor edge the herd was grazing on moor grass and blaeberry. Three heads lifted and turned when Bounce stepped from the trees. The antlers of the switch-horn, out-topping his erect, donkey ears, were clear of velvet, and white in the fading light. Bounce, butting playfully at his mother's flank in greeting got a tuft of her peeling winter coat on his horns. When Dance capered up to him, inviting him to play, he chased her through the heather, in wide circles and figures of eight, till the clouds purpled in the afterglow and the last of the light gathered in the clear, turquoise sky.

The deer spent the clear, moonless night in the open, and by sunrise were grazing on the headrigg of the Stane Farm hayfield, where the old year's stubble was still straight and brittle. Bats were flying from the woodside trees to spend the daylight hanging by their feet from mouldering walls and rafters. In the morning gloaming they had hawked among the trees, avoiding every twig and branch in their path by hearkening to the echo of their own voice-squeaks thrown back in warning, and eluding the claws of One Eye who often hunted the bauckie-birds at the last and first of the light.

The switch-horn wandered into the wood, but Bounce couched in the heather beside his mother and Dance, to feel the early sun before seeking his harbour. When the moon appeared above the trees, pale in the light of a sun three hours risen, they filed into the wood, with Dance bounding ahead and Bounce butting heather in the rear. And tragedy came to the roe family in the sunny morning, while grouse crowed and the cushats crooned in Glencryan. . . .

Dance was ten paces in front of the doe, on a well trodden run along birch saplings and hazels, when she was jerked suddenly to her hindfeet, screaming and striking out with her hooves—snared in a slip-noose of fencing wire, suspended from a branch overhanging the trackway and cunningly arranged to take the head of a deer.

Instantly, the doe's flag spread, and she bounded forward in alarm. Bounce stopped short, tossing his head and stamping with a foot. Choking and terror-stricken, Dance plunged this way and that, wailing and screaming and straining at the wire; but at each bound she was pulled up and thrown to the ground, with the noose drawn more tightly on her neck. Ere long she was lying on her side, panting, moaning and whimpering, with foam on her lips and her tongue hanging dripping from the side of her mouth. But she could not ease the strangle-hold of the wire, for her head was held clear of the ground by the noose.

So she cried out piteously, while her eyes bulged and the saliva came frothy with her breathing. In Glencryan, many ears heard her cries. A carrion crow, standing by the woodcock's nest in the beechwood, listened for a moment, with flat head tilted and beak dripping yolk, then went on with his sucking of the woodcock's eggs. One Eye's mate, heaving on her nest in a flat-topped pine, opened wide her lustrous eyes and crouched down closer on her wriggling owlets. Suddenly, the switch-horn buck bounded into the thicket, with ears and nose asking questions. From the heather came two second-year does, in peeling coats, to watch and wonder, and stamp their feet in sympathetic disapproval of the scene in the thicket. So, when a fox skulked upwind seeking information with his nose, he turned back without viewing, and sneaked quietly away from such a dangerous gathering.

The doe tapped her fawn with a forehoof, and nuzzled her gently, coaxing her to rise. Then she thrust her muzzle under Dance's flank, and pushed with her head, as if trying to drive her away from the thing that held her. Clearly she didn't understand the meaning of the wire. Yet there can be no doubt she saw it, for the roe will stop short at a cotton thread stretched across its run, and a thread so placed is seldom broken. The strange does drew close to sniff in puzzled solicitude; but after half an hour the problem was still unsolved, and Dance, foaming at the mouth, was dying.

Man smell on the wind sent the deer bounding away—all except the doe, who stood till the man was near. Bounce ran in the switch-horn's slots as far as the beeches, then turned away through the birch swamp, barking and leaping high to check his back trail with his eyes. In the beechwood a crow slipped quietly from its nest in a crotch, and flapped away low through the trees. The doe barked twice, like a terrier, as the man approached her fawn, stamping till he was close enough to see the colour of her eyes. Then she ran off a little way into the scrub. When he bent over Dance she started running in circles, crashing through the undergrowth and barking as she landed after every fourth bound.

The moocher cut Dance's throat with a quick stroke of his knife; then he gralloched her. He broke her legs at knee and hock, cut off the trotters and put the body in a sack. All the time he was watching the doe, but he decided against resetting the snare, believing she would avoid the runway after that day. The doe stopped circling when he left. Once he was clear of the wood, she began to call for Dance in low, hoarse tones, running hither and thither, but avoiding the thicket with its smell of blood. When Bounce came to her at sunset she was still searching for her fawn.

At darkening they were joined by the two strange does, and browsed and grazed along the route they had followed the previous night. The switch-horn was casual with the newcomers; Bounce fed close to them, fussing. By midnight the doe had forgotten about Dance; at least she gave up seeking her in the wood. In the night, when One Eye was flying in with his seventh rat from the farm stackyard, a fox found what lay in the thicket, and carried two trotters home to his cubs, leaving the paunch and entrails for the carrion crows. John Long found the cubs playing with the trotters when he went to plant gins at the den-mouth nearly three weeks later.

The doe did not pass through the thicket again; she went round it, and a loop was added to the well-worn runway. For three days the dusky carrion crows held revelry on the remains of Dance, and in the sunshine flies buzzed in the thicket. When the keeper saw five crows rising from the feast on the third day, he searched where they had risen, and smiled slyly at what he found there. Very cunningly he set two gins, and caught two crows, which he hung by their black feet from a branch in the beechwood; then he replaced his gins as carefully as before. But his sets took no more crows, for the birds had seen, and remembered, and none came to the thicket again.

Bounce did not understand that Dance was dead; he knew only that she was no longer there, and sometimes he looked for her at dusk. In the nights following her death he stayed close to his mother, feeding much on sparse new grass, blaeberry shoots and tender leaves of hawthorn; but each morning, while she grazed with the buck towards Glencryan, he sought the Braeburn larches for a little while to rub against the stems with his peeling antler spikes. Sometimes he rubbed cannily, like a dog being kind to an ear; and sometimes he scraped viciously till the young larch bark was scaling and the furred velvet curled on his dags. Then, when the owls were folding their wings for the day and the first cushats croodled in the trees, he left to join the doe at the harbour in Glencryan, cantering across the wet, threshy pasture where the long-nebbed whaups were calling.

The varnish was running on fat, up-pointing chestnut buds before the last lappets of velvet fell shrivelled at his feet beneath a massive beech tree on the fringe of Braeburn.

That morning the sunrise came moist and cramasie after a night of smirring rain, and every briar spike and thorn held its bead of sparkling water. Birdsong trickled from the trees with raindrops shaken loose by the singers' feet. The pines were touched with red and the light glanced bright on the rain-washed silver of the birches.

A black crow, with a nest in a high fork of the beech, flapped down as Bounce circled the rain-darkened trunk prodding and rubbing with clean antlers white and hard as ivory. While the deer gathered green moss and dark stains on his new white antlers, the crow sidled up to the cast, rotting velvet and snatched it in his ebony beak. Bounce stabbed at the beech trunk, grunted, and charged at the crow; but the wily bird made two leaps sideways, gathering his mouthful, then was up and away with a harsh *caw* of triumph and a whicker of wings to his wool-lined nest in the naked fork. While he wedged the velvet into the closely laced sticks, beside a leather boot lace and the Sports Edition of a Glasgow evening paper, Bounce gave expression to his new-found truculence by stabbing viciously at the unyielding tree.

When a second crow flew into the beech, with a beakful of wool gathered from barbed wire which had hooked it from the fleeces of sheep, he danced back, hock deep in brown matted leaves, shaking his head. Water had showered down on him from slim branches shaken by the crows. He scratched an ear with a hindfoot, rubbed the inside of his left foreleg with the tip of his right antler spike, then leaped away sideways, head down and stiff-legged, as if suddenly startled. But he stopped just as suddenly, relaxed and unstartled, to bite briefly at green trefoils of wood sorrel peeping above the brown leaf carpet. He was full of high spirits that morning, a young buck freshly cleaned, with the first colours on his horns and the sun in his blood.

But high spirits took second place to native cunning when he at last turned to go, and he minced warily from the cover of Braeburn, with ears seeking sounds and nostrils open to the wind. To his forward ear came lark-song, the crowing of grouse, the far cries of gulls. Curlews, winnowing low, trilled unseen in misty hollows on the moor. Overhead, the bleating of a snipe, as it circled in the vaporous blue with outer tail feathers spread like lesser wings. Near at hand, other snipe were feeding in the soggy, thresh-grown pasture, probing for creepy crawlers in the lairie.

Fox smell came to him on a wayward eddy of wind, and in a moment his nose placed the Glencryan vixen near the straining post at the headrigg fence. Across the wind, and closer, he got the scent of a hidden hare, which was sitting up, ears erect, keeping track of the homing fox. Closer still, he could own the trace taint of a wetted weasle, hunting unseen in a vole creep under the pleated tangles.

Remembering Dryflatts, Bounce kept his nose on the fox till he found her by sight. There was a steely glitter in his great limpid eyes as he loped slowly across the pasture with no thought of flight, no itch to quarrel, but in no mood to be hustled. The hare edged aside, revealing herself, as the buck passed close, then fled with flattened ears towards the open moor. Bounce kept track of her with an ear till she was clear away, without nose or eyes relaxing their watch on the fox. He was fifty yards from the woodside fence when the vixen trotted along to head him, with nonsense in her eyes and half a rabbit in her jaws. Bounce stopped short to ponder, with one hind-foot buried in a crumbly, steaming moleheap, momentarily irresolute. Then the spring came into his legs, and he bounded forward, chin down, to carry the argument to the fox.

The Glencryan vixen was sleek, sly and seven, battle-scarred and deer-wise, and mischievous when the odds were to her taste. But she was not foolhardy, except in defence of cubs, when she would have parted with her life to save one little woolly tail. At sight of the white-pronged buck coming on to meet her, she ducked under the fence, dropping her half rabbit beside a stob to leave her teeth free for action. When Bounce leaped the fence, with forehooves held to chest and inches to spare, she snaked down the wet ditch under a screen of briars, brambles and sodden, plaited grass, till she had the cover of a squat, many-stemmed saugh bush rooted on the lip.

While the buck pranced above her, crackling in the brushwood, she stood belly-deep in red, staining water, pondering her next move. As a ponderer she had few equals among foxes, which is why she was seven. She knew all there was to know about the vagaries of roe, and realised at once that this amazing sapling was not to be bluffed or chivvied. She realised it more than ever when Bounce, thrashing the saugh branches with his dags, drenched her with water and wet scliffs of dark soil sliced from the ditch top by his hooves. So she crouched to wait him out, with eyes closed to slits and tusks bared to the gums, and all fox-nonsense completely forgotten.

Bounce soon tired of the ploy, because he had not been roused to anger, but simply pricked to a display of courage by a fox threatening to bar his path. Presently he wandered off, wagging ears that itched with water. In the first birch thicket he stopped to rub his antlers against wet, moss-scummed stems, tinting them further till only the tips were white. When the vixen clambered from the ditch he heard her, and whipped instantly about. But he made no attempt to renew the chase. Instead, he watched her skulking below the fence to retrieve her rabbit. She left a trail of orange-red smears on the grass, for her legs were soaked and dyed with slimy water from the ditch.

Pheasants were crowing and wing-flapping when he reached the first of the pines. He found the doe rubbing vigorously against One Eye's tree, ridding her flank of loose winter hair. Above her, the owl was huddled on his perch, *wee-wicking* gratingly with both eyelids drooped. He had been treed all night by the rain, and had nothing in his craw. His three owlets, ravenous with thirty hours of fasting, were stirring restlessly under their mute, sleeping mother, cheetering for mouse or vole or shrew, or rat or baby rabbit.

The doe, ignoring Bounce, slouched away to her lair among tall, sere grass and brushwood near the nest of the owls. Bounce watched her scraping her bed with a fore-hoof, then found his own lie under a lone scrub oak less than six roe bounds from One Eye's tree. The owl was still *wee-wicking* querulously on his pine roost, with one foot drawn up among the feathers of his breast and his sound eye lidded against the glare of the sun.

Cushats were crooning *Coo-coo: cu-roo*, in full-throated, rhythmic chorus before the trees were shorn of their rain-sparkle by the warmth of the sun. Frail wood anemones, bending and a-tremble with every puff of wind, opened hair-streaked, lilac petals, and were visited by flies greedy for their pollen. The pine tops quivered, glinting blue. One Eye fell silent. Bounce, muzzle to flank, closed his eyes. His touzie coat sheened over, drawing the sudden heat of the sun. His sides heaved gently to his breathing. He slept. In sleep, he wagged ears irked by sun-loving flies. And in sleep he heard that which brought him instantly awake, with nostrils seeking answers to confirm the warning of his ears.

Two hundred yards distant, where sun-touched leaves of chestnut and sycamore spread their pale green among the pines, crows were yarring as they circled above the wood. Overhead, the whistle of cushat wings, and the clatter of others leaving perches to the promptings of the crows. Crackle of brittle twigs and the thud of hasty feet among the blaeberries told of a rabbit in headlong flight, careless of the manner of its going.

Such were the tidings received by his ears, while his brain was yet asleep. Startled to wakefulness, his only movement was the lift of his head to bring his nostrils full on to the wind and his eyes to the eye-level of a sitting hare. Yet again his ears heard the footfalls of a man before his nostrils found the scent of man and dog, far out on the main Glencryan runway, now elusive, now strong, in the treacherous ebb and flow of the soft morning wind. With ears opened forward, nostrils wide, and eyes unwinking, he waited for a view; and presently he saw movement among the trees.

John Long, the keeper, was striding along the runway, with a gun in the crook of his arm and a black dog at heel. . . .

Bounce crouched with chin level, taut, untrembling, his ears erect and unmoving under the assault of flies. Suddenly, the dog stopped, reaching across the wind with his wet, black nose. A woodcock, alarmed by his snuffling, rose in swerving flight from a heather clump near the trail, where it had squatted since sunrise inside a circle of its own droppings. The bird registered as movement in the eyes of Bounce, but neither eyes nor head turned to follow when it passed the side limit of his seeing. At thirty yards distance the dog became excited, feathering on a line. Bounce's long lashes swept down once in a fleeting blink; but he did not stir. He knew he hadn't come that way.

At twenty yards a cock pheasant exploded into the air from under Long's feet, leaving droppings to tempt the tongue of the dog while he rocketed above the trees, all bronze and autumn crimson in the sun. The keeper snarled the dog from his drooling, shouting: "Heel! Tweed! Damn!" and Bounce tensed for flight, knowing the dog had a nose. The young Labrador hearkened momentarily to the rattle-tinkle of wings, then fell in behind, with head bowed and pink tongue flacking.

Presently man and dog were gone from his nose and eyes, but not from his hearing. He relaxed, curling tongue round his upper lip. He tilted his head, without rising, and lifted a hindfoot to scratch. The hoof had barely touched his ear when he threw up his head, alerted by the wild, frenzied yelping of the dog.

A rabbit came scuttering through the brushwood, head up, ears flat, showing the whites of its eyes. The rabbit was a doe, with sparse fur on belly and teats newly suckled. On her heels came John Long's retriever, who was a gamefinder of repute, with a nose for runners, but deaf and a rioter when he got away on rabbits.

Rabbit and dog passed within ten paces of the deer, but Bounce sat close, showing heart-flicker on his hide, while Long swore, and whistled to recall the dog. One Eye leaned over to stare when the rabbit raced under his tree. Tweed crashed in the brush, running open-mouthed with hanging tongue, yelping more and more excitedly as his quarry drew away. Mould flew with the leaf flinders from under his great pads, and the noise of him sent up every ear in Glencryan. The rabbit, waywise in the swampy birch thickets, went through unerringly in spurts and bounds, hopelessly snarling her trail; but the chase ended for Tweed at the first patch of bog. His more than eighty pounds of bone and rippling muscle were too much for the sphagnum, and in a moment he was up to the oxters in treacherous ooze, mute and terrified, flailing wildly with forepaws to fight his way clear.

Bounce had followed the chase with his ears. He knew the meaning of Tweed's sudden silence, and watched for the dog returning. One Eye drew himself up long against the trunk of the pine, with razor-edged beak almost hidden in the feathers of his breast. Ground disturbance rarely startled the owl to flight. Cushats were already circling back to pitch on green chestnut sprays, or flap down to flat, flimsy nests in dark pine tops; and settling wings and crow-talk told Bounce there was nothing more to fear in that part of the wood.

Presently Tweed appeared, walking slowly with the crow-waggle so typical of his breed. Stinking, watery ooze dripped from the hairs of his belly, and legs and thighs were plastered with black, shining glaur. Tail and head drooped dejectedly, but the nose that never lied still sniffed on its ground arc, scent-gathering, by habit. A shrill whistle from Long at that moment made him bear left in answer, and Bounce saw he was headed for the thicket where the doe was lying.

She had been listening to his movements, and knew the line he was taking; but she made no move to break till he was almost upon her. Tweed was completely taken aback when she leaped up and way, for his nose had no word of her till it drew in the reek of body scent released by her rising. Long whistled again, and Tweed trotted on without lingering to smell or hanker after the doe, for he was as rock-steady to deer as he was riotous on rabbits.

Bounce rose from his knees when Long's footsteps passed beyond the reach of his hearing, and loped away in search of his mother. On the birch fringe he met the switch-horn, who had lain close, chin to ground, while the dog was rioting. His sparsely-pearled antlers were brown and green on the shaft, after much scraping against saplings and the branches of fallen trees. Bounce reached to prod playfully at the old buck's matted flank, but was warned off by hog grunts, a foot stamp and horns presented in threat. So he turned away on his own, all foxy-red and lichen-grey among the scraggly, sunlit birches, and found the doe lipping thorn leaves at the northside fence.

She received him coolly when he approached, and threatened when he fussed. Together they browsed along the wood edge on birch twigs and young leaves of thorn, drinking from the ditch in the noonday heat when the leaf shadows were still. Afterwards, they settled to rest and chew cud under a dark, triple-stemmed spruce more than a hundred roe bounds from their morning harbour. Ten feet above their heads a cushat was brooding twin squeakers in golden down, on a dense spruce frond layered deep with fallen twigs.

The flapping of cushat wings in the spruce brought them awake while the sun was yet four hours from setting. The cock bird flew out as the hen pitched in the tree, and Bounce heard the peeping of the chicks as they reached up to be fed. While the cushat fed them, lifting and bowing as she pumped curd from her crop into shovel-beaks delving in her gullet, Bounce rubbed hair tufts from his haunch against a green, mossed stem. The itch of loose hair was commanding, and he left matted tufts on ground and tree after each rubbing.

The cushat flew to earth, to pant open-beaked after feeding her chicks. The white feathers of her neck were raised with the strain of disgorging. She had no dread of deer but, when Bounce pranced towards her, with head lowered in mock threat, she flapped back to her nest to elude him. He wheeled about to watch her, with muzzle uptilted; he paused, wondering if she would return. And, suddenly, he was stamping; he was tossing his head; the cushat had shaken down spruce dust and scalings, which filled both his eyes.

He spent the last of the daylight alone, lying up among old, crumpled bracken near One Eye's tree. When he arrived, the owl was already a-wing, seeking voles among the blaeberries; hunting in sunlight because there was rain-famine and a dying owlet in his nest. Three times, while Bounce slept and the moon's pale crescent dipped down the sky in the wake of the sun, he carried fat voles to his mate; and twice he was harried and scolded by song-birds when he flapped, moth-like and silent, into the glare of the open.

At sunset, the owl swept to his pine roost with a fourth vole in his claws. Bounce heard him *wicking* to his mate, and the hen's throaty *wee-wick* from the nest in answer to the food call. Overhead, the sky was still blue as a dunnock's egg, and the moon's talon silvering above the sunfire in the west. In the wood, pheasants were crowing. The woodcock was circling on his eve-flight, dark against the luminous sky. Bounce jumped up from his knees as One Eye switched his prey from claws to sickle beak before flying in to his mate. The birds were mewing and displaying on the nest when he left his lair for the evening feed.

In the pasture the doe was grazing; he could hear the brush of her feet moving in the threshes. Rabbits were feeding out from the wood. The doe shook her head at him, unwelcoming; so he wandered off on his own, browsing along the edge of Glencryan. All that night he foraged alone. Thrice, before dawn, he rested to chew cud; once under the lane-side elms at Stane Farm, and twice in the Wood-of-no-name. There he met other roe, cudding under cover; but he did not join them when they went out for their last feed of the night.

At first light he was cantering across the Glencryan

pasture, with paunch well filled and a chill wind on his muzzle. Ice filmed the ditch-water, thick enough to fracture when he reached down to suck; there had been frost in the last moonless hours of darkness. Erect flower buds of horse chestnut, like tiny fir trees half hidden among unfolding leaves, were nipped and burned.

In the wood, One Eye was hooting as he folded downy wings on his roost; he had killed five voles and two shrews since the stars brightened in the frost. He was *wicking* drowsily to himself when Bounce came to harbour, but he opened wide his one lustrous eye to note the deer passing under. Bounce was scraping his bracken bed when the woodcock flew over, croaking on his brief morning circuit. A cock pheasant cu-cupped; larks were singing. In the leafing scrub oak a tam tit called *hooeet*, heralding its arrival from the deep tropics of Africa. The deer settled with legs upgathered, hindhooves to forehooves, muzzle to flank, and slept.

Grey vapour clouds trailed across the sky at midmorning, and the wood was sunless. From a field at Stane Farm came men's voices and the tinkle-tinkle of a bell; the men were planting potatoes. Bounce sought the doe among the beeches, and found her snipping twigs from down-sweeping branches. She looked round when she heard him, but when he moved close to browse she drove him off, butting at his haunches with her head. Bounce stood for a little while under another great beech, lipping twigs still sheathed in brown, then pranced up to her again, with head turned sideways and chin tucked in to shoulder; but again she drove him off, butting as before.

All that day he slouched in her slots, to the far end of Glencryan and back to his morning harbour, while cushats croodled, and the potato bell tinkled and paraffin smell came in waves on the wind. Bounce was perplexed; he could not understand that the time of parting was near.

At night she would not allow him to graze beside her, so he sought the company of the switch-horn, who was pulling at willows growing through the woodside fence and dingling the wires with his antlers. But before starlight, when One Eye was mousing over the tussocks, he loped away across potato fields and cornfields to the Wood-of-no-name, and spent the rest of the darkness in company with another yearling in similar plight.

Summer drew its plaid of green over the trees, and the beeches shimmered and glinted gold in the sun. The purple clubs of the ash shook their pollen on the wind; leaf and catkin quickened on the oaks; green fronds of new bracken, like shepherds' crooks, uncurled among the red, withered tangles of the old. Tam tits built domed nests in bracken stool and grass tussock, and lined them with hen feathers from Stane Farm and downy pigeon feathers gathered from dark, dusty spruces. Twin owlets flew in Glencryan when the blue bells glowed in drifts of purple; their youngest nest fellow had died on a night of famine, and they had eaten him in small pieces torn from the body by the beak of their mother. All day cuckoos called; and at dusk the nightjars churred while One Eye swooped at voles scurrying in the narrow lanes between the drills of green corn.

One morning Bounce sought his mother in vain. She was not in the wood. In the night, while he was resting in Braeburn, she had slipped quietly away, travelling by the Wood-of-no-name, Fin-me-oot and the bank of the Luggie Water, to the spot near Thirteen Beeches where she had once rescued the buck fawn of another doe.

EACH DAY THE RAIN FELL SOFTLY—THE FINE, WARM
summer rain—drenching, soaking, seeping, and the
gumlie water flowed in the deep peat ditches. The moor
was one with the sky. Sheened purple, the moor grass lay
before the rain; the bog cotton dipped its silken tassels;
from birch leaf and heather bell the water dripped, colour-
less and unsparkling under the dreich, grey clouds that
smoored the windless sky.

One night the wind shook the heather, and the bells
shed the rain they had gathered by day. To the west the
vapours rifted, revealing a blue pupil of sky with the
moon as highlight. Owls hooted, and shook rain from
feathers, and flew out to seek small birds in leafy bushes
because no voles were running in the sodden blaeberries.
Out on the moor the curlews skirled when moon and stars
were bright in the rain-washed sky. Dawn came, tremulous and dripping, with the wind in the trees; grouse
crowed; and when the nightjars had wavered away to
roost for the day the moon was already extinguished by
the spreading fire of the sun.

Grouse, crouching low, led downy chicks along hoof-
marked sheep walks under woody heather stems when the
last clinging rain-drops were flickering with rainbow fire
in the rays of the sun. From an old grouse butt, near the
ruins of Hoolet Nest steading, a roebuck rose, dark as the
peat on which he had been lying. His ivory-tipped dags
were weathered to the hue of pine bark; the points of his
cletts bleached with much walking in wet grass and

heather; his white flag quilled and soiled after the rain. His slim, knock-knees were stained and skinned with wet peat, gathered when he knelt at settling and rising.

Bounce grazed on moor grass, and snatched at purpling twigs of heather, till his rain-darkened coat dried out to foxy red in the heat of the sun. The peat flaked from his knees, leaving the hair scuffed and discoloured. The soft, dense fur of his flag fluffed out and whitened like the downy heads of bog cotton waving in the wind. At mid-morning the wind backed and died; the sun beat down with torrid heat; the birches quivered, drooped and were still. Bounce, panting, went to drink from a pool of peat-filtered water in a grassy hollow on the edge of the heather.

At the pool three grouse were drinking—two hens in grey, frayed plumage and a red chesty cock with fine crimson wattles. Twelve chicks at the age of fluttering were copying the old birds, sipping water and swallowing with up-pointed beaks, sneezing droplets from nostrils and getting the down of their throats wet with drips. One hen lifted her wings and ruffled her feathers when she saw the deer approaching, but she stepped aside, chuckling, to let him drink.

He drank long and thirstily, with ears listening in different directions and eyelids drooped, ruffling his own water image reaching up to him from the sky-blue in the pool. Deer and grouse had taken no water during the rainy days; now in the heat they were drinking their fill. The grouse would not drink again till the following morning. At sunset they would cram their crops with dewy heather; by then their gizzards would be empty of water, and in the night their droppings would be dry.

The grouse moved away from the pool to brood chicks. Five burrowed under one hen, four under the other; and the mahogany cock, squatting, lifted his wings to take three. Bounce threw up his head, champing, with his lips dripping water. The grouse shuffled wings, blinked, and were still. The hen brooding five chicks had lost her mate, who had been caught by a foot in one of Long's gins, and killed and eaten by Smoky Joe, the hoodie crow, who lived at Hoolet Nest. The gin had been meant for the feet of Joe, who was old and wise, and had perfect feet unmarked by any kind of teeth, and Long guessed the story when he found the feathered foot of a grouse where he expected to find the foot of a black-and-grey crow.

It was now long past Bounce's resting hour, but the old butt had suddenly lost its appeal. He was troubled by vague longings; irked by a strange restlessness. The wanderlust fever was burning in his blood. With ears pricked forward he stared towards the hills, taut, motionless, straight-necked, sun-silked, till his dwam was disturbed by the harsh calling of Smoky Joe, who was being harried by curlews over Hoolet Nest. Bounce licked his shoulder, lowered his head in mock threat at the sitting grouse, then loped away in the direction of the steading, travelling on ears and eyes because there was no wind.

At the doorless doorway of the long-ruined steading he stopped to rub a haunch against the masonry. The doorway was overshadowed by a massive horse chestnut, whose branches reached far into the roofless steading. High up among the dense foliage Kree, the kestrel, was sitting in the flattened nest of a crow, brooding five tiny chicks in white down; and presently Bounce heard Yellow Foot, her mate, calling to her from the mouldering wall above his head. Yellow Foot, who had a grey tail tipped with black, called *Wree-wree-wree; wree-wree-wree*, and Bounce, looking up, saw Kree fly to him and take the mouse he was holding in his beak.

Yellow Foot flew away, and Kree returned to her chicks. Bounce scraped with his teeth between blocks of masonry, for the sake of the lime in the mortar, then snatched at green chestnut fronds which he pulled in and chewed with relish. Bees were humming in the chestnut blossoms, led to the stores of nectar by yellow and crimson spots on the petals. Kree, standing with yellow feet firmly on her mouse, stopped tearing to peer down at the deer who was rearing on his hindfeet to reach the lowest leaves. After thirty seconds she returned to her mouse, tearing off small pieces then tilting her fierce head sideways to place them in the beaks of her chicks.

She was brooding, with the sun bright in her eyes, before Bounce left the steading, travelling across the rough moor pastures towards the green cornfields and neat, drilled potato fields of Skeoch Farm. Yellow Foot was hovering above the big hayfield, with grey tail depressed and head down-pointed, searching for movement of mouse in the green deeps of grass. He saw the deer in the pasture, slouching through the threshes with peewits and whaups running alongside with spread wings, turning him from their chicks. Then he saw a mouse and dived from his pitch.

Bounce got his first view of Yellow Foot when the little falcon flashed into his line of vision on his downward swoop. Instantly, he eyes focussed the movement, and held. At the last moment, when it seemed he must crash into the hay, Yellow Foot opened wide his long tapering wings, arresting his descent and directing the clutch of his foot. Bounce stood at gaze till the falcon flapped up again, with a crushed vole in his claws. No curlew or peewit rose to assault him when he flew overhead on his way to Hoolet Nest, for they knew Kree and Yellow Foot, who shared their ground, and had no reason to fear them.

During the long day of sunshine and blue sky Bounce lay up on the hay, cudding and dozing, while flies' wings whined like a circular saw and Yellow Foot carried seven more mice and voles to his mate at Hoolet Nest. At sunset, with the light flowing in waves across hay tossing and leaning before a chill wind from the east, he turned back into the pasture, to feed on grass, and cuckoo flower and purple self-heal. While he grazed, curlews and peewits rose to drive off a pair of marauding crows, which had sucked many eggs and eaten many chicks since their own big-gaped, big-bellied gargoyles had hatched.

The crows yarred and snarled, and the curlews dived at them, calling *cu-cu-lu; cu-cu-lu; yoi-yoi-yoik* and striking with their long, curved beaks. The black raiders soared and flapped slowly away. Bounce grazed up to a big hummock of moor grass, which was hollowed out on top; in the hollow were four large, green, pear-shaped eggs. While he grazed, a whaup came running, head down, through the tussocks, on a zigzag route. She ran on to the hummock, straddled the eggs, and lowered herself on to them, with her beak stuck in the grass. She chortled *coorwee* when the buck nibbled close, then laid her beak along the line of her back, and slept. Other whaups planed down, trilling, on outspread, motionless wings, and soon there was silence except for the whisper of wind in the rushes.

Dusk fell like a violet cloak, diaphanous, earth-scented; the eve star brightened in the sky. At Skeoch Farm owls were calling. Bounce trotted through the hayfield and across a drilled field where turnips were brairded. In the shadowed drills rabbits were running, moving under cover from hedge-bank burrows to the cornfields near the road where each night they ate down the green growth of many days. And each night they grazed on unmolested, for all the Skeoch foxes had died in Long's gins.

At the roadside thorn hedge Bounce paused to check the wind, standing belly deep in wild liquorice with briar spikes scratching at his neck. From the farm closs, a hundred yards away, came the voices of men, but he could get nothing with his nose for they were out of line on the wind. Upwind, there was no scent of danger, so he followed the hedge to a gap, jumped through and crossed the road. Stuart of Skeoch, coming to the closs mouth at that moment to lead out a car, saw him cross, and wondered at a roe being so far from cover.

In the field were sixteen dairy cows and a string of yearlings, all brown and white Ayrshires, sleek and well paunched with grazing on the rich second-year ley. Bounce reached down to bite at clover and leafy cocksfoot, but was immediately hustled by the herd, which bore down on him in line abreast, snorting with tails held high. He cantered easily ahead of them, following the fence along two sides of the field, then jumped a wire-topped drystane dyke into a scrubby haugh, dotted with rush clumps and stunted birches and much churned up by the snouts of hogs. At the bottom of the slope, a burn flowed on its muddy bed through great thickets of gorse.

While the cows shambled round their field, Bounce loped down towards the gorse, stumbling on the ploughed-up ground. A big white sow appeared suddenly from a lean-to of corrugated iron on the edge of the burn, followed by nine black and white piglets barking in alarm. The grumphie rushed at the deer, with mouth open and ears flapping like sails; and Bounce, stumbling on a folded sod snagged with a root of gorse, was bitten before he could regain his balance. Her teeth scored his shoulder, drawing blood, but before she could bite again he had leaped up and over her, and was splashing through the burn while she weaved about in a frenzy seeking him in the opposite direction.

On the far side of the burn other pigs rushed out squealing from crude wooden shelters—yeld sows, fat gilts and a huge Tamworth boar. The boar launched himself at the deer, mute, lip-licking, deceptively swift, a mountain of bone and muscle who could have swept any buck off his feet and broken him in the twinkling of an eye. But Bounce, now pig-wise, bounded aside and watched him turn short after his rush. For one wild, insane moment he was tempted to use hoof and antler, but when the boar came on again, champing his jaws, he turned away at speed towards the netted fence which was the end of the pigs' world.

And it was here he met an unexpected foe. As he cleared the netting, he smelt dog smell and dog breath, and twisted in the air to face round at the touch-down. A black and white collie was bellying up to him with deep-throated growls. Bounce would have stood, for he feared no single dog of the size, but at that moment he heard Stuart's voice raised in anger calling "Moss! Moss! Come in Moss! Come tae me, Moss, you bastard!" The combination of man and dog melted his courage, so when the collie made his final rush he side-stepped with head down and turned for the open moor. He could not know that the man would not follow.

The collie was fast, fierce and cunning, but a coward deep down in his heart. He had killed rabbits and rats, as well as hens, and his teeth had met many times in the throats of sheep. But he had so far escaped punishment, and many better dogs had died for his crimes. He had been sneaking away on a poaching foray when he saw and smelt the deer running before the cows. This was his first wild, hooved quarry, and his heart warmed to the chase.

Bounce ran with lips parted and nostrils wide, in tremendous bounds that took him at high speed across the moor. Behind him, the collie ran in his slots, with head low and tail flying, keeping touch with his nose; the deer was running close to the wind. Bounce leaped a succession of wide, deep ditches, running full with dark, oily water; through thick clumps of threshes where redshanks were nesting; across wide belts of tall, silver-crusted heather that clutched at his legs. Though he was on strange ground, and bleeding, with half his wits harking back to the dog on his trail, he negotiated treacherous sheughs and broken fences and moss-ringed dubs with uncanny skill.

After six hundred yards the collie was still running his line, mute and unwavering, but fast losing ground. Once a blue hare rose, and once a brown, running low with ears flat from the line of the hunt; but the dog was not lured from the trail. Bounce turned on a slant at the top of a heathery knowe and kept bearing right across the heather beyond. He was shaping across the wind, and down, taking his scent out of the dog's nose and getting the collie's in his own.

The collie yelped as the scent faded, and was at fault till he topped the knowe and saw the figure of the buck in the gloaming. From there he hunted by sight, getting the line confirmed every now and again from the scent lying in Bounce's slots. But he was losing the race. He knew it; and Bounce knew it. His yelping changed to the long drawn out howl of failure. Then came mishap. . . .

The heather thinned, giving way to moor grass and rushes and massed dwarf birches. Bounce saw ahead a drystane dyke, and braced himself for the leap; but he failed to see the wires on top till the last moment, and was taken unawares by the nature of the ground. The soggy peat held his hooves at the take-off. He hit the top wire with a hindfoot and fell, gathering the lower stand with his fetlock, and in an instant was hanging upside down with the hoof held in the cross-over. He struggled in a panic, treading with his forehooves and kicking out wildly with his free hindfoot. Stones toppled from the dyke top; the wires quivered and hummed. But still the crossed wires held. And, presently, the collie was rushing at him, with teeth bared and tongue flacking, eager for the worry.

With a final, despairing lunge Bounce thrust himself into the air with his forefeet. For a fleeting instant he hung poised above the dog. Then he fell forward again, scuffing his white chin on an embedded stone, bruising his shoulder, and collapsed in a fankle of legs. But his hindfoot was free!

He was on his side, dazed, momentarily winded, when the dog leaped, growling, with forepaws stretched to hold. The hot breath engulfed him, almost sickening him with nausea. But, as the long teeth reached for his neck, he turned his head, struck backwards, and struggled to his knees. A weasel, peering from a dyke cranny, *chip-chip-chipped*, and doubled back like an adder recoiling. But he reappeared almost at once, knowing he was safe from the dog, driven by the abiding curiosity of his race.

The collie, thrown off balance by the antler stab in the ribs, clawed desperately at the buck's withers, with webs spread, trying to hold him down. In that position he was stretched, with his belly taut over Bounce's head. Bounce, thrusting himself from his knees, took the dog in the belly with his dags, ripping, almost gutting, him, and tossed him writhing to the ground.

On his feet, he wheeled to face the foe, with chin tucked to throat and antlers presented forward. The dog was rocking on a hip, yowling and whimpering as he flicked his tongue along the cut from navel to breastbone. Completely preoccupied with his wound he was blind to the further menace in the buck's threatening pose. Bounce, bracing his knees, lunged forward, stabbed, pushed on, and pinned him against the dyke. He kicked and twisted, howling in pain and terror, as the buck stab-stabbed, with all the fury in his heart and all the power of his shoulders behind the blows.

At last the dog collapsed, whimpering, bloody, broken, with nineteen stab wounds on his body. Bounce danced back, retching, and vomited green cud and stringy slime that dangled from his lips. He was almost ready to drop with sickness, rage and terror, and wobbled on his legs. So he let the dog squirm away, followed by a weasel running the dyke top, and lurched drunkenly into the first cool, dewey scrub.

All night he remained on foot, walking short distances, then standing for long periods with head drooped and mouth open, drooling ropes of spittle. At morning twilight he crossed a wide, green, moorland pasture, tussocky with rushes and yellow-dotted with tormentil, where a herd of milking cows was grazing. A hedgehog was snuffling over the pressed beds of cows, snatching tiny beetles and licking up globules of milk that had trickled from heavily stocked udders in the night. Bounce held away to avoid the cows, in case they should harry him, and left the field by a hedge-gap where a sheep was hooked by the fleece. He followed the hedge ditch till he reached a burn, where he stopped to suck water before lying down on a knoll, which was ringed by flowering gorse and close-cropped by the mouths of sheep.

At first light he rose and crossed the burn. Two partridges were running in circles on the far bank, clucking agitatedly while a brown rat squatted under a gorse bush eating their eggs. Bounce scanned the rolling ground ahead, a wide expanse of moor grass and heather and waving bog cotton. In the brightening sky curlews were trilling. Three-quarters of a mile away, on the skyline, stood a roofless, crumbling steading, noisy with jackdaws which nested on piles of sticks stuffed down behind the lathing on the walls.

Bounce lingered to nibble at lance-shaped leaves of comfrey growing from the lip of the burn. All the time the partridges raced up and down, voicing their plaint. Presently the rat, having eaten its fill, rolled an egg from the nest and started to push it through the grass with its snout. Hearing it, Bounce laid back an ear. At the same moment, a white bird drifted past on wings as noiseless as his own ground shadow. The ghost-owl checked in flight, tilted, swooped, and clutched in the grass with his feet. The grass shook to the buffeting of wings; the rat squealed thrice as its life was squeezed out by the needle-tipped talons of the owl; then Bounce saw the white shape flap up and away, silently, like a great white moth, towards the ruin on the horizon, with the limp prey dangling from his feet.

The buck followed at a slow walk, reaching the ruin when the sun was high. About the steading the turf was springy, close bitten by the teeth of rabbits and sheep. Here were signs of roe—tell-tale foot slots and droppings like coffee beans in little heaps on the sward. Bounce snipped off a yellow dandelion head, which he twirled between his lips while he stood stock still to listen before making a wary circuit of the ruin.

Jackdaws were clacking in the walls, feeding chicks behind cobwebbed lathing; others were flying out and in, seeking and carrying food. In one jackdaw nest sat a sleeping barn owl, brooding close on two jackdaw eggs and six of her own; she had driven out the little silver-eyed crow after it had started laying. On a whitened stone in the rain-washed chimney her mate was standing on one foot, wide-eyed, drawn up long, with a milch rat under his claws.

Bounce pushed his head through a glassless window frame, watched by the grave, dark eyes of the owls. On the rubbley, grass grown floor lay the skeleton of a roe, with sinews and hair tufts still clinging to the bones. The roe had sought shelter in a storm when the door was open, but it had blown shut in the night and made him prisoner, and after long days of hunger he had sickened and died to provide abundant feasting for the black, scavenging crows.

During the heat of the day Bounce rested among stones and nettles against the northside wall, beneath a hole from which rubble had spilled and which now held a pied wagtail's nest with chicks. All day, while tortoiseshell butterflies thronged to the nettles and the deer slept or cudded with eyelids drooped, the wagtails flew in with food for their nestlings in the wall. At first they were alarmed by the presence of the buck, and flittered along the wall top calling *chik-chik-chik* with their beaks full of flies; but, when they realised he was not to be feared, they were soon hovering round his antlers, snatching insects above his head.

At dusk, the white owl flew shrieking from his perch in the chimney, and Bounce wandered out to graze. During the short, moonless dark he lingered near the steading; but at daybreak, with the owl purring on the window-ledge and shadowy whaups rising in song-flight in the gloaming, he was irked anew by the urge to wander. When the first swifts screamed overhead under the paling stars he was far out on the heather, travelling at a lope towards the high moor skyline, where birches trembled in the dawn wind.

The deep heather sleeked his slim legs with dew, and freckled them with the old husks of faded bells. When the sun rose, he was in a fenced wood of spruce and larch, cudding with his flank against an ivied stem. From the wood, the ground fell away gently—tree-dotted, green with grass and corn, brown and hazed violet, yellow where charlock was showing. Far down, a winding ribbon of mist lay still over canal and tree-lined banks and farms and grazing cattle. Rooks were flying from the mist to pitch in black clouds in pasture and turnip field. At the farms cocks were crowing. Bounce sought out a thicket when five cock pheasants, crowing, flapped down from tree roosts and sprinted from the wood with tails held high.

At nightfall he left the wood and cantered towards the canal, halting every now and again to snatch a hasty mouthful of grass, or dock, or bramble, or hogweed. Peewits wafted aside at his approach, uttering low, vibrant, hirstling cries. Across these fields had once marched the proud Roman Legions; here the Imperial eagles had spread their wings in the sun, to view for a brief moment the land they failed to conquer; here, too, marched Wallace to the glory of Stirling and the shame of Falkirk, and here the great Highland war pipes had skirled triumph and challenge before the clansmen followed their Tearlach to the final infamy of dark Drumossie Moor.

——— 13 ———

BOUNCE FOLLOWED THE CANAL FOR A MILE, SNATCHING hasty browse from thorn and willow growing along the towpath verge; his appetite was fykie with the growing fever of the rut. Flies and beetles were thick in the air about his head and the bauckie-birds were hunting them above the water. Peewits, disturbed by capering heifer beasts and polled black bullocks, were crying fretfully on the other side of the canal, and the buck could hear the swish and hum of their wings as they dived and twisted in the air. When the cattle beasts winded the deer they came rushing to the water's edge and stood in line abreast, with heads down, snorting query and challenge, and churning glaur with their hooves.

The cattle shambled along the far bank to keep in touch, with heads down and tails held high. Bounce turned away from the canal where the ground rose in a long slant to a hayfield. Halfway to the top he halted to direct ears and nose to the haugh on his right. His ears registered the sound of lapping and to his nose came the smell of brock. The badger was drinking from a grass-puddle which was fed by water seeping under the dense gorse in the haugh and flowing thinly over surface pebbles: he had just eaten a rabbit from a snare and his thirst was salty.

The badger shook his head and returned to his snare to snuffle over leavings; he had rabbit wool in his claws and wisps stuck with dried blood to his snout. Bounce, seeing the dark, moving smudge of him, shook his head without anger, then trotted up the ridge kicking his heels in the air. Not even the fire of the rut could rouse him to threat display against a badger. At the ridge-top he found a gap in the high thorn hedge and leaped into the hayfield over sagging, rusted wires.

A thin crescent of moon rose clear and honey-coloured as he entered the field. At the far end were twelve rucks in line; over the rest of the field the hay was coiled. Bounce stopped beside a coil to sniff, and suddenly— above the sweet scent of hay and the earth scents distilled by the dew—the smell of roe urine came strongly to his nose. Another buck had been in the hayfield before him! Bounce snorted and grunted and stamped with a forehoof; then, with ears forward and nostrils wide he sought further knowledge. But neither ears nor nose could find present sign of deer, so he minced forward into the field and stamped a forehoof at each spot where the vanished buck had stood.

In the night he prodded rucks with his dags, and bit at dew-wet clover, while the moon's crescent silvered and a tawny owl hunted the coils. Irked by a strange, commanding thirst, he drank five times before dawn from a wide ditch where the water was freckled white with shed petals of elder. After each visit to water he lay down to rest in the shadow of a ruck; but only once did he doze with muzzle against flank. At break of day, when the owl was flying to roost with one leg down and a young rabbit in its claws, he left the hayfield by a gate where the soft ground was tyre-marked by tractors and slotted by the hooves of deer. By sunrise he was five miles from his starting point—trotting through hogweed and fireweed on a cornfield edge, with briars and brambles clawing at his flank—headed for a big wood on a long ridge where rooks were flying.

Pheasants were crowing in pine tops in the heart of the

wood; from the fringing belt of tall ash and sycamore cushats flew out on whistling wings, to pitch in fields of corn where others were bending stalks and pulling ickers from the tap-pickle. Whitethroats and tam tits were already flittering in the brambles, seeking food for chicks. Bounce turned into the wood, stumbling among brambles that sprawled over a crumbling drystane dyke. Beneath the far-spreading branches of the first great sycamore he stopped to lick coronet and fetlock, and rub muzzle against forelegs; the bramble tendrils had pricked, and left barbs in his skin.

The wet grass under the hardwoods brushed the hedge-row weed-seeds from his legs as he loped towards the dark pines beyond. Between the last tall sycamore and the first of the pines was a heathery hollow in which mist was lying. Bounce vanished in the mist and crossed with only antlers showing. When he emerged he paused to scratch ears with hindfeet before trotting along a ride between tall pines and spruces. The ride opened into a wide, heather clearing, ringed by high rhododendrons and with three pines in the centre. Bounce edged warily under the screening branches, and sniffed. When he had sniffed, his ears shot up and he trembled; the wind puffs were bringing scent and the scent was roe.

Under a lone sycamore on the other side of the clearing a roe doe was standing, with head up, chin level and eyes unblinking; in the spruce gloom behind her was her fawn of the year which the buck could not see. Bounce snipped off a sprig of blaeberry from the clumps at his feet and walked stiffly towards her twirling it in his lips. At the centre pines he halted again, querying with his nose and setting his ears forward for sound. Then, as if suddenly reaching a decision, he chewed and swallowed the sprig, tossed his head, barked twice like a dog, and danced sideways towards her.

The doe was four years old and had small, unforked antlers which she had never cast, or cleaned, since they started sprouting in her first December. The velvet was scuffed and worn, and scarred where old wounds had bled. Horned does are rare among roe, and some men say they are barren; but the doe under the sycamore was in milk and the fawn running with her was her own.

When Bounce was still a dozen paces away the doe walked out to meet him, with chin down and flag-frill twitching. Stranger though he was she was ready to receive him as a wooer. They met muzzle to muzzle and, after a fleeting roe-kiss, the doe held up her white chin for the caress of Bounce's tongue. Bounce licked her till she lowered her head to prod, and met her antler to antler when she pushed. When he disengaged and side-stepped, and ruffled the hair of her flank with his dags, she shook her head, reared, lunged forward at the touch-down, and dunted him playfully between the eyes. Bounce, grunting, re-engaged her, and they circled head to head in mock combat.

Suddenly, the doe stepped away to snatch at heather. She bit off a leafy tip, rolled it between her lips, reared, pirouetted, and spat out the morsel. Bounce watched her with his eyes, while ears and nose made a circuit check of the clearing. Discovering nothing on the wind he went back to the doe, and prodded her flank till she started to trot; when she was in her stride he ran on her offside, touching her flank with his antlers and forcing her in a circle round the pine trees in the clearing.

Bounce drove her round five times before slowing pace, then walked her round once, kepping her on the outside like a collie heading sheep and prodding at her flag to keep her moving. By then they had trampled out a clear path in the heather, which formed a rough ellipse—twenty-five yards from end to end and eighteen across.

After the sixth circuit Bounce pranced up to the pines and gouged bark with his horns; the doe frisked to the sycamore and ripped mouthfuls of feathery grass growing at its base. A blue tit, poking with its beak under the curling bark, whirred away when she rubbed her neck against the trunk, and its white dropping splashed on her head. Then Bounce chivvied her from her rubbing, and they started a second love-chase on the same route as before.

The deer circled the pine trees twenty-seven times before breaking off the game. The sun was now rising red above the serried spruce tops; the air in the clearing became suddenly warm. Fat bumble bees arrived with the sun to crawl over the heather, and dragon flies, rustling gauzy wings, flew from green spruce fronds to hawk insects along the tree fringe.

Bounce rested on foot when the race was over. His slim legs, wetted by heather, were steaming; his flanks heaved gently; his pink tongue was showing. While he stood leg-licking the doe disappeared into the spruces, and presently he saw her returning with her fawn. With head down and sideways he raced to join them. He touched noses with the doe, sniffed quickly over the fawn, then led them into the sun-shot darkness of the wood. He was now the young master buck taking charge of doe and follower. . . .

At sunset the deer returned to the clearing, leaving the fawn, milk-sated, in the spruce cover a little distance away. They played the love-game till the afterglow faded and the last yarring crows were rocking flat-footed on perches with beaks pressed into shoulders and breast feathers puffed over claws. The doe gathered her fawn, and during the night the little herd browsed along the woodside and grazed in pasture and hayfield, resting and cudding among rucks in the open. At first light the doe put her fawn down in the wood while she trysted with the buck at the clearing. And there they raced round the pine trees until sunrise as before.

For three days Bounce was lord of the herd, and coupled three times with the doe on the ring. They were days of hot noon sun and bloodthirsty clegs, with nights of heavy dew and clover scent and meadowsweet fragrance, and misted mornings when the vapour lay in the hollows, white and moveless and concealing. Men cleared the hayfields when the sun was high, and the deer, browsing or resting in the wood, heard their voices and laughter, the barking of dogs, and the ear-dulling roar of tractors. At night, when the herd went out to feed, they found and ate damp crusts of bread and dew-wet cigarette stubs which were lying in a hayfield.

Rain fell heavily on the third day before the deer went to the clearing, and all night the wood was filled with the sound of running water. By daylight the rain was a steady smir. The mists brooded low over the trees. Water dripped from the spruce tips, pocking the ground-fibre; under the layered fronds the dark earth was dry. The coats of the roe were sleek and rain-dark and the white fur of their flags was soiled.

Bounce was rubbing itching ears against forelegs and scratching shoulders with antler tips when he heard the barking of a buck in the wood. He grunted and threw up his head, with slim neck rigid and ears cupped forward. The newcomer did not bark again. He had heard Bounce's grunt and could smell him on the wind, and was making a wary approach to see what he was like. He came as noiselessly as a cat, touching no branch with his antlers; and Bounce, being upwind, could not smell him. But, presently, he saw the movement of him among the rain-sheened rhododendrons. He stamped smartly with a forefoot, and the spring was in his knee. The intruding buck thrashed savagely with his antlers in the rhododendrons, shaking water from leaf and branch and drenching himself in the shower. When Bounce started his mincing, challenging walk across the clearing the buck burst dripping from his cover and pulled up short to await him.

The challenger was an old, crafty buck, heavier than Bounce, with a full head of six points; but he was past his prime of antlers and the pearls on the shafts were sparse. Bounce stamped with a forefoot when he was within twelve paces of the intruder, then reared high in threat with his ears laid back. When he touched down his back was arched and his forelegs stiff. The six-pointer tucked in his chin, and strained back, gathering his muscular hindquarters for the attack. And in that moment Bounce charged with antler spikes forward.

They met brow to brow, with forefeet clear of the heather, and when they touched down they shook their heads like terriers worrying a rat. *Click-click! Click-click-click!* The antlers were striking with a sound like dry sticks.

The click of antlers brought the doe to the edge of the clearing. The six-pointer, seeing her, tried to run to her, but was headed by Bounce who raked fur from his shoulder with his dags. Stung to instant fury, the old buck wheeled with the speed of a viper striking, lowering his head and stabbing upwards in one continuous movement to take his attacker under his outstretched neck; but Bounce was quick of eye and nimble, and met him head to head, with forelegs bent and taut; and again the antlers clicked. They danced back, and re-engaged; they feinted, and parried and stabbed; they circled with locked antlers, grunting, while their breath vapoured on the air.

Then the old buck, realising he could not get past the vicious sapling's guard, fell back on sheer strength. He locked horns, braced his thighs, and pushed. And Bounce had to yield. Back, back, back he was driven. But he fought every inch of the way, trying to gather his hindquarters for a lunge, till he was forced almost on to his haunches and in danger of being pinned to the ground. He was saved by a hollow, into which he fell backwards. Before his opponent could follow through to stab him he was up and away, unmarked and blowing, and with a hard glitter in his eyes.

Away, yes; but not in flight. He ran twenty paces and turned to fight again. The six-pointer yapped and came bouncing to the assault, and once more the head shook and the antlers met.

Click-click! Click-click-click!

Bounce was stabbing savagely, and his unforked spikes twice scored his opponent's forehead, furrowing grizzled fur without breaking the skin. Both bucks were grunting. They were matched for fire and courage. But, gradually, the six-pointer's greater strength had its effect. Bounce was driven back, and forced round broadside, and suddenly felt the rake of antlers on his flank. So he broke away, mute, and ran through the drenching spruces, pursued by an opponent barking in anger and challenge.

Cushats clattered from high spruce tops as the deer crashed in the brushwood; rabbits scuttered for burrows because they thought a dog was barking in the wood. Bounce broke from the spruces into a bracken-choked ride and followed a well marked deer-path through the tall, green fronds. On the opposite side the ground rose steeply, with beech and sycamore on the slope and high, red-barked pines on top. Bounce started to climb, but stopped halfway up the slope, on a moss-grown outcrop of whin, to watch for his pursuer.

He waited till the six-pointer reached the bottom of the slope, then tucked in his chin and charged. The old buck, righting himself after a hoof skid on moss-scummed rock, was caught off balance, and for one brief moment was at the mercy of Bounce. Bounce dirked him viciously in the ribs and sent him rolling in the bracken but did not follow through. Instead, he raced for the ridge-top knowing he would be outmatched in the heavy cover.

He paused, blowing, on the crest, heartened by his success. The six-pointer, winded with the dunt in the ribs, did not come right on when he reached the ridge: he began to circle warily, grunting, and stamping with a foot. Bounce circled with him, half-rearing with forelegs taut. Their eyes met and held. Then both pawed pine needles and leaped to the attack. *Click-click!* The contact was fleeting. The six-pointer drew back swiftly and feinted, then side-stepped and turned, and caught Bounce on the flank as he lunged forward to stab. And this time the old buck's top points were tipped with blood.

Bounce felt the sting of the wound, and the jolt almost halted him as the air locked in his lungs. In that moment of shock he accepted defeat. He tried a final, over-the-shoulder hook with his dags, then broke clear and fled down the other side of the ridge, with pine cones and pebbles stotting behind. He slithered the last ten feet, slicing the wet soil with his cletts. More cushats crashed from the oaks on the level as he raced for the burn, with ears laid back and tongue-tip showing from the side of his mouth. He splashed across the burn, stepping high like a trotter, breasted down and trampled through the valerian and meadowsweet on the opposite bank, and bounded across a haugh of antler-high birches into a roundel of pines.

But he was not allowed to rest. The six pointer arrived in the roundel on his heels, with his big ears flat and his slim neck rigid. Bounce lowered his head in threat, but did not wait to engage when the old buck charged. He tossed his head and ran, using the pines as a foil, but was

headed three times in the treeless glen beyond and forced
to cross antlers in a fighting retreat. When the old buck
at last broke off the chase, the deer were six hundred
yards from the clearing in a direct line and a mile and
three quarters by the way they had come.

That day Bounce harboured in a wood called Hackamore, which was dense and dark, and suited his mood.
The massive crowns of horse chestnut and sycamore, out-
topping the dark arrow-heads of spruces and the tousy
crests of unthinned pines, gave colour and form to the
hard contour of the wood. Under the close canopy of
trees the thickets were warm, and in many were the
pressed seats of outlying rabbits.

In the first rage of defeat Bounce thrashed at low,
brittle, barkless pine branches and broke them off with
his horns. The cut in his flank was irking him little; he had
rubbed hair over it, and the hair, matted with dried
blood, was sealing the wound. But there was fury in his
heart, and when he surprised a halflin fox pawing a
yowie beside a windfall, pretending it was a mouse, he
leaped at him without warning, striking out with his forehooves. The astonished fox snaked clear of the hoof-stroke,
and bellied away under brushwood and fern-covered
windfalls, with the buck prodding fronds in his rear and
shaking raindrops in showers from down-clutching
branches.

Later in the day Bounce was put on foot by the Hackamore Farm collies, Lint and Lassie, when they came to
gather the cows for the milking; the dogs liked to mix
rabbiting with herding and always made their cast
through the wood unless checked. Bounce, lying two roe
bounds from the pasture fence, heard and smelled them
coming in on his rear, and was up and away before they
reached his lair.

The dogs barked their discovery and started to chase.

But Colin McLeod of Hackamore, standing atop the farm midden with his mouth full of fingers, called them to order with a piercing whistle which lifted them at once from the warm deer line they were so eager to follow. They were back in the pasture, nipping cows' heels, before the buck reached the cornfield hedge on the far side of the wood.

When he realised he was not being followed Bounce returned to the pasture fence and scraped a new lie where he could view the field. He was not greatly alarmed by the coming of the dogs. During the night he made many visits to the cornfield, without once nibbling at the yellowing grain. His craving was for eyebright, which grew in thick carpet on the ground, and had tap roots stealing sap from the roots of the corn. Bounce ripped up entire plants, munching with obvious delight, and lipping in the ragged trusses hanging from his jaws. He was in the field again at daylight, when the first swallows were hawking low over the rustling corn, cramming his paunch before going to his lair by the pasture fence.

The dogs came during the morning, and again in the early evening, but were kept from the wood by McLeod's warning whistles. Bounce kept track of them in the pasture with his ears. When the cows returned after the evening milking the sun was hot and frayed of edge in the rain-washed sky; swallows were hunting high above the trees; cushats croodled in the sunlit tops of spruce and pine. Bounce rose when the midges were dancing in clouds beneath the woodside trees and wandered into the sun-shot gloom of Hackamore, rubbing flanks against pine trunks and stabbing bark with his dags. While woodcock flapped silently above the spruces and owls shook wings for flight he snipped off leaf and twig of elder and chest-nut; then, when the owls were a-wing and the wood was dark, he trotted away to bite at fading flowers of stitchwort on the cornfield edge.

It was then Lassie came foxing through the wood in search of deer. . . .

Bounce leaped away, startled, when she came yelping from a fern clump, then realised she was alone and stopped short to face her; she had no man smell behind her and he was not afraid. He waited for her, head down, watching her with his eyes; but the lowered front was a familiar pose and the bitch refused to attack head-on. Instead, she started to circle, trying to come in on his rear. Bounce, with ears and nose plotting her movements in the waving corn, stepped round with her, pivoting on his fore-feet. And, presently, having completed her circle, Lassie broke cover on the edge of the corn.

She was beginning to realise she would never win close enough to bite unless she started him running. So she bellied down and barked, then glided forward four paces in threat. Her weight was still forward when Bounce ran at her grunting, but she was agile enough to evade antler stab and hoof-stroke, and escaped to the cover of the cornfield hedge. At that moment Lint arrived to join her and Bounce fled because he knew he was no match for two of them.

The collies, yelping their excitement, gave chase, but were slowed by the corn. Bounce was fifty yards ahead when he jumped the wire-topped drystane dyke between cornfield and pasture. In the pasture he cantered through ragwort and threshes and tall, spiked thistles, rousing peewits that swept high over his head then tumbled down in humming flight to harry the dogs. *Wees-weep; wees-weep!* The birds distracted the dogs while the deer sailed through a hedge-gap into a seven-acre field of cabbages planted for sheep. Beyond the cabbage field was a deep gully, with gorse and thorns growing on the slope. Bounce turned short round a gorse bush, cantered thirty yards on his back-track, then leaped far to one side and raced for the cover of the reed thickets on the burn bank at the bottom. And there he couched, facing the open, to wait for the dogs.

Lassie arrived alone; she had lost Lint in the cabbage field where he had flushed, and chased, a big jack hare. The bitch stopped, at a loss, when she overshot Bounce's dead-end line. She whined and fidgeted. Then, being a collie, born to herding sheep, she started to cast, with tail high and feathering. But she made her cast too near the end of the line so did not regain the scent, and presently she trotted away to look for Lint.

Bounce did not return to Hackamore. When the bitch was beyond his hearing he rose and browsed on alder leaves till the edge was off his hunger, then slouched away along the burn to continue his quest.

When the corn is yellow, and the wild raspberries in the hedge ditches dark with ripeness, the rut of the roe is over. Barks of challenge and the shock of antlers are for other summers. The fire flickers and dies in the veins of the bucks, who seek solace and renewed strength in seclusion, leaving does and followers to go their way till the equinoctial gales are spent and the first horned moon of October rises clear to greet the winter stars.

The whaup clans, gathering for their outward flight, were sounding their parting pibroch when Bounce viewed Heatherfield from Cowther Wood, on a morning of blue sky and sun-glare and flaffs of wind running like mice feet through the dry, trembling corn. The lush, green foggage of the Cowther hayfields was stippled with faded brown where rucks had stood. Sheaves of corn leaned against the hedges where end-riggs had been scythed to prepare the way for tractor and binder. The light flowed with the wind over the green waves of the potato drills; and the waves had a lilac crest, for the potatoes were in flower.

Bounce walked slowly along the rutted lane by Cowther Wood, shaking his head against his halo of flies. In the tree shelter the sun was warm. Cushats crooned drowsily in the trees. Tam tits and whitethroats were flitting from bramble tendril to spiked briar, or fluttering in the lane-side tangles of fireweed and cow parsnip, knapweed and yarrow and yellow rattle, seeking food for fledged broods perched on gorse spray and birch twig out in the heather. Bees sang their honey-song of sun and sweet nectar as they crawled on the heather bells, cramming their leg baskets with pollen.

The voice of Cairns of Cowther came suddenly from the road, and when the farmer appeared on the hairpin bend with a collie at heel Bounce cantered away through heather and birch scrub to the roundel on Heatherfield where he was born.

14

ONE EYE, THE TAWNY OWL, WAS SITTING ON A ROTTING
birch stump in a clearing in Glencryan, with his
single lustrous eye staring into the sodden blaeberries and
the wet wind ruffling the feathers of his back. After ten
days of rain the ground was waterlogged; new waterways,
fed by overflowing sheughs and ditches on the moor,
wound in gleaming network under the trees, forming
leafy pools in the hollows; the Glencryan burn, racing
smooth as a mill lade, bank full and gumlie, had
flooded the birch thickets, drowning rabbits and field
voles in their burrows. One Eye, treed by the onslaught
of rain in the long, dark nights, had eked out a living
snatching tit or shilfa from saugh bush and birch scrog
by day; now his craw was empty and he was wild with
famine.

That morning the daylight came misted and silver, with
purple glint on the bracken and rain smirring fine as
gossamer in the clearings. Voles, driven from creep and
burrow by the rising waters, had scurried in the night to
higher ground, to ridge and knoll and hummock and peat
bank. They were driving new tunnels under the blaeberries beside One Eye's perch, and the owl, hearkening
to their scraping, was ready to swoop and clutch at the
first glimpse of bright eyes or blunt face or rain-wet fur.
But when he spied movement at last, and was inflating
his throat ready to pounce, his ears heard another sound
at his back, and he turned his big head quickly to discover
the cause.

Two deer were walking slowly through the pines, splashing along a flooded, leaf-strewn runway—a young buck with five-inch antler spikes and a greying coat, followed by a slender doe of his own age treading in his slots. The deer's slim legs were plastered with mud above the fetlocks. They had crossed a squelchy potato field to reach the wood, sinking to knee and hock in the drills where drains were choked, but the water on the deer path had cleaned their cletts, leaving them with footless stockings of Stane Farm glaur.

Bounce minced to a halt and shook his head at the owl. One Eye drew himself up tall, rolled the eyelid down twice over his seeing eye, then bowed on his perch, clicking his beak. The doe pricked her ears; Bounce grunted and spashed water with a forehoof. The owl's throat pulsed, and his low-pitched, querulous *wee-wick* was a hint of mounting anger.

The deer reached down to nibble at wet blaeberries. Instantly the voles' scuffling ceased. One Eye swayed on his perch, blinking and beak-clicking. The voles started scraping again, reassured by the instinct that enables them to distinguish friendly movement from the stealthy tread of the hunter. The owl stood tall, with neck stretched and wings half-open, his head weaving up and down, from side to side and in circles. Then, when the deer had their heads up, shaking and munching wet sprigs of blaeberry, he launched himself without warning at the doe.

She reared with the downy wings buffeting at her head, and back-tracked squealing when talons like fish hooks raked her face. One Eye, flapping and *wee-wicking*, clutched and struck with his feet while she plunged and kicked, but was shaken off when she bounded headlong into the wood. The owl, correcting balance, turned steeply and glided back to his perch, brushing the blaeberry tips with his wings. Bounce, who had leaped high at the doe's first cry, tried to butt him in the air and prodded at his perch when he pitched. But One Eye's fit of fury was spent. He leaped up as Bounce charged and flapped to a pine branch, and there he sat, chortling his throaty *wee-wick* and clicking his beak while the buck raged and stamped in the blaeberries.

The anger soon died in Bounce and he left to seek the doe. He found her in the beechwood, under low, far-spreading branches, with head down, trembling. She had dark smudges on her forehead where she had rubbed against the wet, black-veined trunk. Blood was bubbling from fine cuts above her eyes, and gathering in a tiny pool inside her left lower eyelid where the owl's claws had pricked; but her sight was not impaired. Bounce sniffed her solicitously and ruffled the grey hair of her neck with his spikes, and presently they lay down together on the springy leaf carpet under the beech.

They had joined company in Heatherfield in the blue and gold harvest days following the rut—the yearling doe too young to be wooed and the precocious buck who had stolen three days of love-making in his second summer— feeding at dusk and dawn on leafy grass and clover, on leaves of thorn and briar and bramble and elder, on sweet raspberries and crimson haws and the rich, waxy-vermilion berry clusters of the rowan. By day, they had harboured in the birch roundel when the sun was warm and in the open heather when the sky was overcast. Then, when the rains came, heavy and seeping, and there was no dry couch on Heatherfield, they had travelled by Thirteen Beeches and Fin-me-oot and the Wood-of-no-name to the heavier cover of Glencryan.

At noon, the doe rose and rubbed eye against knee; blood clots were sliding down her cheek with clear fluid brimming from her eyelid. Bounce wandered away, per-nickety, lipping birch and beech twig, grass tuft and

heather clump, leaf and catkin of alder, without eating.
Then he found a briar, aflame with scarlet, rain-sheened
hips, on which he fed till the wood turned suddenly dark
and hail like hazel nuts struck painfully at his eyes and
face. While the storm lasted the deer couched in upright
posture under the beech, facing the trunk, with their
backs to the driving wind and hail.

The hail pattered to silence and the leaf carpet was
spangled with white. The western sky flared to brass and
ochre; the wind died; the trees quivered and were still.
Dark clouds hung poised above the wood, flushed with
electric blue. Wrens hid in old nests in the roots of windfalls; tits sought refuge in tree holes; pheasant and woodcock crouched under dense heather clumps. No bird
called. The air was taut; the wood still.

Then the lightning flashed its daggers in the sky. The
clouds were riven by antlers of blinding rainbow blue.
The thunder crashed and rumbled; the trees shook; and
presently the rain came down, straight and sheeted,
drenching heather and bracken and blaeberries, cascad-
ing from beech crotches, and sleeking dark the grey coats
of the deer. Leaves moved with the moving water along
the winding channels in Glencryan, and the rain-pools
overflowed from the hollows to send new trickles creeping
into the flooded birch thickets.

At darkening, nervous of the rising waters, the deer rose
and cantered through the pines to the narrow moor road.
The roadside ditch was running bank-high under dripping hazels. Overhead the moan of the wind in the tele-
phone wires; everywhere the lap and splash and swish
and seep and gurgle of rioting water. Bounce led the way
along the crown of the road, lashed by driving rain and
staggered by gusts in the tormented dark. At the cross-
roads the deer trotted knee deep in rushing water. A bold
leap through a gap in the hedge and they were on flooding

stubble, with two hundred yards of squelchy field to cross to the dark haven of Dryflatts.

Under the dense spruces the rain was mist and spray, but the surface peat and needles were puddled and the roe could find no dry place to harbour. Bounce forced his way under the tossing spruces and trotted through the wood till he was halted abruptly by the Glencryan burn, which was racing deep and swift and could not be crossed. Sticks, branches, boulders, seed baskets and dead sheep were rolling and tossing on the current and the roots of the bank elms were awash.

Bounce splashed along the bank in near panic, with the doe following meekly at his heels. Beyond the last spruces the burn had overflowed and the water was spreading in Dryflatts. The deer did not turn back into the wood. They crossed sodden levels of cotton sedge and moor grass, breasting through scrub birch and saugh till they reached a high knowe topped with beeches. Bounce led the doe up the slope on a slant, and together they lay down among the bracken on the crown.

Storms of rain in the night kept them harboured on the knoll. When daylight came, wind-shaken, two acres of Dryflatts were under water. Stubbles and pastures were flooded, and bullocks stood at field gates, plastered with mud to the knees, bellowing in alarm. The potato drills were canals in which gulls were swimming. The deer browsed and cudded on the knoll in the rain of the day, and when night fell their sanctuary was an island, for the Glencryan burn had inundated the levels for a hundred and fifty yards from its bank.

When the next day dawned, sunless and wet with drifting vapours, Bounce tried to leave the knoll. But when he minced warily into the water he found himself at once out of his depth. Instead of swimming for the wood he turned about and struck out with his slim forelegs till he touched ground again on the knoll. Dripping water from flanks, legs and belly, he circled the slope with the doe and found they were marooned.

But they were not alone. Rabbits were moving among the bracken. Seven black-face hoggs stood under the beeches staring glassy-eyed across the water. Musk taint came heavy and rank from an outcrop of whin over-looking the burn, where a big fox was sitting looking half-size and spindly in rain-sleeked fur. The fox made no move to run when the deer's heads appeared above the rocks from below, and Bounce turned away without display or threat. The deer did not see the stoat crouched on a low, splintered beech branch; nor did the stoat snarl when they passed below. He was up there out of reach of the fox's jaws, and water-fear had, for the moment, tamed his savage heart.

The rain ceased, and the beeches dripped leaves and water. The stoat sat up on his branch to lick wet fur; the rabbits pawed faces and chewed cud of dung pellets licked from their vents; the fox continued to sit, slit-eyed, on the whin outcrop watching the burn. He knew the water would fall first at the bank.

The deer chewed cud under the beeches, but their paunches were slack and they soon felt the irk of hunger. The doe sought the whin outcrop, where she had noted gnarled rowans and berried dog-roses clinging with root systems exposed, and the fox yielded unsnarling when she came boldly forward. She reared where the fox had sat, forehooves to breast, stretching her slim neck to lip scarlet hips; but before she could grasp her first mouthful she lost her footing on the treacherous rock and plunged forward with forelegs flailing. Skidding and lurching down the face of the outcrop she was pulled up hard and suddenly when a foreleg caught in the Y-cleft of a rowan branch. Her squeals brought Bounce, set for war; but when he found her he was at a loss, for there was no enemy to challenge. He could not understand how the doe came to be dangling from a tree, with her hindfeet barely touching the rock. . . .

Black crows pitched in the beeches, attracted by the doe's sobbing cries. The fox skulked to the bracken cover; the rabbits fled. Squirrel-like, the stoat sat up on his branch, with ears tuned, hearkening. Bounce circled the outcrop, bewildered, in a frenzy, unable to help. And, presently, the doe fell silent, and hung limp, with neck grotesquely twisted and left ear touching her flank.

By mid-afternoon she was hanging unmoving, with tongue far out and hazel eyes staring. Only when Bounce prodded her gently at intervals did her body sway, and then she would kick feebly with a hindfoot.

Men's voices in Dryflatts an hour before darkening sent the crows flying out in alarm. Stuart of Skeoch and his shepherd were seeking lost sheep, and guessed that Highland black-face hoggs, bred on the hill, would be found on the knoll when the levels were flooded. Drawing his glass, the shepherd spied seven of his hoggs; but he could not see buck or fox because they had settled in cover as soon as the crows flapped from the trees.

The glass in the shepherd's steady hands moved slowly as he checked over the knoll, then held still when he pin-pointed the outcrop of whin. After long and critical examination of the hanging deer he handed the glass to Stuart and asked him to look.

"There's a roe caught by a foot in a rowan on that rock face," he said. "She's still living, though. I can see her tongue moving, whatever!" The shepherd was young and Highland, a man who felt undressed if he stepped out of doors without a telescope slung over his shoulder.

Stuart picked out the deer, looked closely, and slapped

the telescope shut. "Noo, hoo could a beast land in a fix like that?" he exclaimed.

As he spoke, his companion was unlacing boots and loosening plus-four buckles from his legs. The farmer looked at him sharply.

"Man, surely you're no' thinkin' o'——"

"It would be a hell of a death to leave her there, whatever," the shepherd said quietly. "And thur crows would have her eyes out before we were fair away. . . ." The shepherd grinned. He hated all crows. "I can undo her in a moment."

"But, man, you'll catch your daith o' cauld!" Stuart remonstrated, more in amazement than anger. "It's a hunner yairds oot, an' the watter'll be three feet deep at the knowe. For God's sake! You're mad, man!"

But the shepherd, stripped to his trunks, was already wading into the chill water.

Bounce broke cover and plunged into the deep water near the burn when the man was still fifteen yards from the knoll. He swam slowly, low in the water, with only his head showing, close to the burn but clear of the strong current. When his hooves grounded he splashed on, leaping and high-stepping, blinded by spray, till he was in the thick scrub before Dryflatts. Then he bounded away, barking, into the wood.

Before the man left the water the fox slipped quietly into the burn and was borne along swiftly by the current till he fetched up on driftwood piled high on the roots of overhanging alders. Then he, too, was away at speed along the potato field end-rigg, dripping water as he ran.

"There's a bliddy menagerie here!" the shepherd shouted to Stuart, before scrambling to the outcrop to release the doe.

Taking the body in his left arm, with the hindlegs gripped securely between his thighs, he lifted her weight and carefully extricated the swelling leg. The body went slack in his arms when she was free, and he laid her down gently on the rock. The trapped foot was ice-cold, but the shepherd could feel faint heart-flutter on her ribs.

"She's alive—but just!" he shouted to Stuart and, slinging the body round his neck, with the slim legs gripped securely in his hands, he stepped warily into the water and waded back to where the farmer was waiting with a shirt and vest over his arm. And when he had dressed, and stuffed his tousled hair under his tweed two-snooter, he pulled heather to make a dry couch for the doe, and laid her down gently upon it, and covered her lightly with brown bracken fronds to shield her from the sharp eyes of the crows.

And when the farmer said: "She'll dee!" the shepherd said: "We'll see," and slung his telescope over his shoulder.

The doe was gone from the thicket before the moon rose, haloed with gold, in a mackerel sky, to cast tree shadows on shrinking waters. She limped slowly and painfully in the wake of Bounce, who had found her at dusk, trying to struggle from her knees. Though he had come to seek her on the knoll he was not troubled by thought or puzzlement when he found her in the thicket. To wonder about such things was beyond his powers.

Bounce did not halt till he had led her to the beechwood in Glencryan. There they chose an open harbour on a mound among fallen branches, springy and soft with layered leaves, where they scraped their lies. And there the doe lay down, breathing heavily, to rest her swollen leg, while Bounce slouched to the wood-edge to browse on dog-hips.

During her lame days the doe did not leave the wood,

and fed mainly on hips and thorn browse along the north-side fence. Three weeks passed before she was able to run, and then she foraged with Bounce for a mile about Glencryan. There were other deer in the wood—the switch-horn buck with his doe and two fawns; but they were harboured at the Stane Farm end and the two parties did not mix unless their paths crossed during the morning and evening feeding times.

Geese and ducks arrived with the east wind's egg-shell ice and cranreuch. Bounce dropped his antlers when the moor was white and the raw sores were pricked by the frost. When January's new moon was showing a silver crescent he had new buds in velvet, and sometimes he rubbed them against the inside of a foreleg. Then the snow came, in soft flakes, silently, and lay deep on moor and iron-hard furrows; and when the moon was bright, and stars glittered in the frost, and foxes were moving shadows on the moor's blue-white radiance, he moved with the doe to harbour in Dryflatts where the dark spruce cover was warm.

15

THE LAST SNOW IN GLENCRYAN, YELLOW-DUSTED WITH pollen shaken from hazel catkins by the wind, was melting into the ditches, and frail wood anemones, rising from far-straggling roots under the deep leaf mould in the beechwood, opened pale purple flowers to sun and raiding flies. Tit, wren and shilfa sang in the wood. Cushats were crooning. Crows yarred and snarled, and cock pheasants paraded round douce hens with one wing down and spread tails tilted. In deep heather, near One Eye's tree, a woodcock was lining a scrape with dead oak leaves, on which her first egg would soon be laid.

Into the wood, when the red-scaled alder catkins were drooping with ripeness, came a big moor fox, with grey mask and a limping gait, accompanied by a fat red vixen with a white-tipped brush. The fox was a six-year-old called The Limper, who had been wounded in a foot by No. 5 shot as a sapling, and the fat red vixen was his mate. She was nearing the time when she would give birth to his cubs and was prospecting for dens in Glencryan.

Bounce was feeding with the doe on moor grass and alder twigs when his nostrils opened and closed on the taint of fox. Leaving the doe, he followed the shachling Limper and his mate far into the wood till they reached an old fox den under a rock near the burn. Both foxes snarled slit-eyed at the buck when they reached the rock, then the vixen vanished inside the den, leaving The Limper to snarl alone. When Bounce stamped a forehoof he climbed on to the rock to snarl in greater safety. But there was no anger in Bounce and, presently, he left to rejoin the doe.

That day, the deer rested and cudded under a shaggy-headed pine tree one hundred roe bounds from the fox den by the burn and twenty from the big badger sett on the edge of the beechwood. Above them, One Eye's mate was sitting close on two white eggs in the old nest of a crow. At midday, when she stood up to lay her third egg, with head drawn in and tail depressed, her wheezing was heard by the deer, who looked up, wondering without alarm. But later in the day she did startle them when she shook out a wet, furry pellet, which rolled over the edge of the nest and hit the doe on the rump. Buck and doe jumped to their feet in alarm, and stood taut and trembling till reassured by ears and nose that no peril was near.

At sunset, One Eye hooted on the wood edge and called his mate to his tree where he had perched with a fat vole under his feet. She flew to him wailing, and the deer heard them mewing in greeting before she took the prey and swallowed it with much head-shaking and grimacing.

Bounce rose, shook his head, licked his knee, and rubbed antler tips against his shoulder. His new antlers were eight inches from tip to coronet, four-pointed and heavy in velvet, with a bud sprouting on the back of each shaft, level with the brow tines, offering a six-point head. Full six points—brow, back and top—come normally to third summer bucks; but good feeding on lime-rich ground, with abundance of hips and other berries, had given Bounce two undersize tines ahead of time.

Two hours after sunset the moon's talon was bright in a starlit sky and the deer grazed out to the Stane Farm lane. They could hear One Eye calling as he hunted the stackyard for house mice which lived in the leets and made meal of the ickers. Fox smell came to them in increasing strength when they were biting off budded twigs of aspen in the laneside ditch, and in a moment they saw the moving smudge of The Limper on the other side of the hedge. The fox passed downwind. The deer could hear his pants and the swish of feathers in grass; The Limper was running with a hen in his jaws. When dogs started barking at the farm Bounce trotted down the lane, rolling a twig between his lips, with the doe at his flank. On the way back to the wood they saw a white shape leaping in the heather, which was a white hen in the jaws of an invisible fox.

Night after night the deer saw The Limper on the moor edge, and often he had hens which he had killed at outlying farms for his vixen in the den by the burn. Bodach, the old boar badger, who had a mate and two cubs in the sett by the beechwood, snarled and grumbled when he crossed the fox's path. The badger was wise, and knew foxes, and men, and dogs, and perhaps he realised in some vague fashion that The Limper spelt trouble in Glencryan. And trouble did come, when irate farmers held council of war and enlisted every available man and rusty gun for an assault against foxes in force.

The big drive started on a windless blue morning, with the cranreuch on the grass and Stuart of Skeoch Farm in charge of the beaters. Rooks were cawing in the Stane Farm elms; larks were singing. Bounce and the doe were on foot near One Eye's tree, moving into the wood for the day, when they heard the distant popping of guns in Dryflatts. The deer halted, with ears questioning, and at the same moment their noses found The Limper at their back. The crafty old fox was mixing his scent with the deer's.

The shooting ceased for a time and the deer settled to cud in the deep cover of the birch thicket with a big ditch at their back. The Limper skulked into the thicket and crawled under brushwood where he could keep track of the deer. When a hare came crashing through the birches Bounce wondered at its flight, and looked out for stoat or dog. But nothing followed. Then cushats clattered out of the wood, flying high and fast in whistling flight, and he knew that men were coming.

Minutes later, his ears heard the footsteps of men on both sides of the wood; the flanking and forward guns were moving into position. A single shot at the wood-end—a sharp report like the crack of a rotten branch trodden upon—sent the rooks circling and cawing above the Stane Farm elms. Then, faintly but sharp, with a harsh edge to it, came the barking of a terrier. Bounce nosed nervously at his flank; the doe curled her tongue over her black, shining nose. The Limper rose and sneaked away into the wood, but presently he came trotting back, tongue a-loll, glancing to right and left, undecided. He had just missed offering himself as a target to the forward guns.

Soon men were coming in line abreast on a wide sweep through Glencryan, and Bounce heard loud voices and laughter, ribald shouts, the clatter of sticks against trees, and the yelping of terriers. Three shots in quick succession, excited shouting, and a fox lurched into the open near One Eye's tree. It fell, struggled to its feet, stumbled through the heather for a few more paces, then collapsed in a dub of water. The Limper, showing teeth in a noiseless snarl, rose and snaked deeper into the birches. Bounce saw a man in breeches run to the fox. He had to cuff away a terrier while picking it up, and when he walked back with the body over his shoulder the dog was dancing among his feet, eager for the worry.

More shouting and stick-clatter followed. Shilfas flew *pinking* over the heads of the beaters. Bounce could see the men among the trees, now less than fifty paces from his lair. The doe trembled, with flag spread, licking her lips. Then, suddenly, the men were stopped by the frenzied barking of terriers far to their left. The dogs were speaking to the vixen's scent at the den by the burn.

Stuart's voice halted men preparing to run towards the sound. "Keep the line movin'!" he roared. "There's guns and men wi' the dugs, enough tae eat ony foxe already!"

Men clouted trees with renewed vigour, and the line moved forward. One Eye, shocked by the rattle of a stick against his tree, flashed from his roost and sailed away in low, gliding flight over the heather. Another stick sent his mate off her eggs to follow. A voice shouted "Hoolets!" then the woodcock was up, all marbled mahogany-red in the sun, flying in swift snipe-flight in the wake of the owls. Bounce flattened when the men were twelve paces away; they would pass a bare roe bound away on either side of him. But, at the last moment, the doe's courage melted. Ere the sticks reached the branches at her head she jumped from her lie and leaped wildly into the birches.

A gun roared as she crashed terrified along the line, and a voice yelled "A deer!" She staggered and stumbled, then swerved bleeding away, and Stuart was shouting: "Whit bliddy eejit shote at the deer? Leave the beast be! The next man tae shoot at deer gangs hame on his feet!"

Sticks shook the branches left and right of Bounce and the line moved past. The man who had fired at the doe was muttering "I never thocht . . ." when a voice hailed Stuart.

"The deer's sair hurted! It canny jump the fence!"

Twice she tried to leap the fence, and twice she was thrown back after hitting the top wire. At her third attempt she jumped clear, spurred by the approach of running men; but she was off balance at the touch-down and, landing awkwardly on whinstones, broke a foreleg

184

below the knee. Maimed and helpless she rolled from the stones, and one of the flank guns shot her at close range as she lay whimpering on the grass.

Before the smoke of the gunshot cleared, Stuart was cursing the men who had run to the deer and left a gap in the line. "Damnation!" he roared, "there's a foxe brekkin' back!" The Limper had seen the gap, and was running for it, with ears back and brush flying. Every gun within range in the line opened fire, and birch bark and heather tufts flew. Pellets spattered dirt in The Limper's face, and one stung him like a wasp in a foot. But he was through—swerving and twisting, weaving round heather clumps and blaeberry cushions, with neck stretched and tongue out, headed for the moor.

Bounce lay still in his cover till long after the line had moved on. The owls came back, then the woodcock, flying owl-like through the pines. From the burn came the frenzied barking of terriers—harsh, skirling barks that spoke of foxes. Men were laughing and shouting. Bounce pricked his ears. The shouting became louder, followed by two loud reports from shotguns and the shock-expelled barking of running dogs. The men's voices became subdued while the dogs barked strong and rhythmically in triumph. Out on the heather fringe The Limper slitted his eyes. He knew that his vixen had been bolted and shot to pieces as she fled.

When his ears told him the men were not coming through the wood Bounce rose warily from his knees and trotted towards the burn. On the field side of the fence were twenty-two men with guns and thirty with sticks. Two were carrying a fox by brush and forepaws, and two were carrying The Limper's vixen with a terrier attached. Suddenly, The Limper called in Glencryan—a mournful quavering cry, rarest of fox calls, that made Bounce stamp with a foot. The men in the field turned to look back, but Stuart waved them on towards Braeburn.

"It's the murnin' o' the dug foxe because we've shote his mate," he told them. "But there's nae use turnin' back. He'll keep. . . ."

Cushats were flying back into the wood before Bounce showed himself at the woodside fence. Blood smell led him to the ditch where the men had hidden the body of the doe, and he sniffed nervously at the spot with ears laid back and white flag twitching. What he felt, no man can know. The doe had not been his mate in the strict biological sense; but she had been his companion. Probably he realised she was dead. Certainly he did not visit the body in the ditch again. And his memory of her had long faded before her flesh was eaten by fox and badger, magpie and crow, and black-banded, scarlet beetles.

Braeburn was driven and another fox shot while Bounce loped far across the moor. Out on the heather he met the switch-horn and his little herd; they had broken back through the line of beaters at the beginning of the drive in Glencryan. Gunshots in Braeburn were faint echoes when he stopped to rest, beside a heathery mound on which was perched a cock red grouse, with head up and tail spread and crimson wattles distended. He was watching other cock grouse, a little distance away, chasing each other in the heather, with wings trailing, calling *Go-whae-ae: go-whae-ae.* Bounce, on his knees, checked round with his ears before settling on his haunch to cud and doze. The March sun was warm and drifting gulls had transparent wings. . . .

An hour later, two lorries and three cars carrying armed men passed along the moor road and stopped on the skyline. Men jumped out and leaped the roadside ditch into the heather, and their voices came clear to the acute ears of the resting buck. Bounce, alerted, kept track of them with ears and eyes, and when he realised they were moving out to Firknowe spinney he rose and bounded right off the moor.

He crossed rough, hillocky pastures and young leys and steaming furrows, then passed through a gorse brake into a wooded glen topped with pines and snowberries. The wet, mouldy slopes were smothered in rhododendrons. At the bottom was a burn, flowing rust-coloured over whin slabs glutty with amber slime. Bounce leaped the burn, sending diving a water vole which had been nibbling a grass stalk, climbed the opposite slope and lay down beside a fallen oak among bracken at the top.

But again he was put on foot, for men came to the wood in mid-afternoon, armed with guns and sticks, well fortified with bread, cheese and cold ham, weak ale and strong whisky. Bounce cantered into the open when the cushats crashed from the trees and rabbits scuttered over oak leaves to the glen. He saw men on the outside of the wood, coming forward to flank the line, but was three fields away before the first gunshot echoed among the trees.

He was following a hedge near houses on the outskirts of a town when he swerved and lowered antlers at the reek of fox. On the other side of the hedge, seven foxes were skulking among fruit bushes in a garden, kennelling in the unlikely place till the big drive was over. A gleg Chinese gander was parading on the lawn, with neck stretched and bill open, hissing like steam at the tods, while shilfas and blackbirds called in alarm from thorn twig and spiked gooseberry spray. The gander honked when the foxes milled, and Bounce minced nervously away.

During the rest of the daylight he harboured in a dis-used quarry among great whin boulders. Guns popped in the surrounding woods till the sun was slanting to its setting and the air grew cold. At darkening, he grazed at a walk to the wooded glen and browsed on oak twigs and snowberry before turning for home. He skirted a village, then turned east past a coup, picking his way fastidiously among tin cans, boot soles, dirty paper, treadless tyres, iron bedsteads and skeletons of perambulators. Here he began to meet foxes returning to home woods after the drives. With the coup stench in his nose he passed through a belt of dusty pines with paper clinging to the branches, and followed a narrow burn into the wide acres of Hackamore Farm. From there he headed true for Heatherfield and Thirteen Beeches. The crescent moon was high and misted when he crossed the Stane Farm pasture to Glencryan, hustled by heifer beasts snorting threat and vapour, with peewits throwing about above his head and filling his ears with wild, familiar music.

— 16 —

A<small>T SEED-TIME, GLENCRYAN WAS DRIVEN AGAIN, BUT</small> The Limper had left the wood and no foxes were put on foot. Men, filling corn and fertiliser into a long, yellow seed-barrow, left the tractor spluttering and puffing blue vapour, and came to the north-side fence to watch the drive. Sacks of corn stood in rows in the field, and empty fertiliser bags were hanging on the fence like washing on a line.

Bounce lay close in a thicket near the fence till roused by a rioting terrier, which came on its own scent wave almost into his nostrils before he broke cover and crashed through the scrub towards the open moor. Sheep, feeding on blaeberries, looked up and fled with the deer through the pines. From the wood-edge rose blackcock in ebony plumage, and pheasants all green and crimson, disturbed by the beaters. A black crow slipped from her nest in a pine and skimmed low over the heather, then circled back with her mate, yarring out of gunshot. Whaups, flying high and fast on even keel, harried the crows over the wood, where pigeons were exploding from dark pine tops. Out on the heather the switch-horn was already lying with his followers, and Bounce settled close by them, in upright position, with ears tuned to the noises in the wood.

The deer did not return to the wood when the beaters moved on to Dryflatts. They lay out in the heather, hearkening to gunfire and the chuckling of grouse, while moss cheepers flew from ling tip to birch seedling carrying

189

fuzz for nests. At dusk, the switch-horn led his herd to pasture and was followed by Bounce who craved the company of his kind. The old buck ignored him so long as he grazed and frisked with the yearlings, but would not tolerate him close to the doe. Twice, before darkness, they danced on their hindlegs, facing each other, and boxed with their forehooves. But Bounce had no fear, and would not be driven off.

Each night he browsed and grazed with the herd, leaving the wood later than the doe and yearlings, and sometimes joining them before the old buck arrived. By day he harboured alone, in the thicket by the fence, while the field was sown then rolled with a ribbed roller drawn by a snorting Clydesdale horse. Peewits, running on the rolled tilth, sought the deepest hoof-marks, and squatted in them, and hollowed out scrapes with their breasts.

The birch catkins were crimson before the swallows arrived at the farm, and soon the birds were carrying mud and straw to the scars of old nests on the rafters of byre and stable. The peewits had lined their scrapes with grass and bents and were laying their eggs, which were sought after by black crows from Glencryan. Bounce, returning to harbour each morning, saw cushats flying down to the field to dibble for corn already brairded. When they had taken their fill they roosted in trees till the grain was pulped in their craws, then flew to their pleated nests in pine and beech to disgorge curd for their squeakers.

After a week of sun and soft rain the cornfield was a mist of green and Bounce began to feel the itch in the velvet of his prongs. By then the switch-horn's velvet was stripping. Bounce cleaned his antlers on the young larches in Braeburn, where he had first rubbed velvet, scuffing the soft bark of four stems and fraying two which had been ringed by rabbits in the winter. While the velvet was peeling he harboured alone in the wood, lying by day in the dark, dusty cover under the larches, and moving out at nightfall, after drinking, to seek the switch-horn and his herd on the moor edge at Glencryan.

One morning he was lying near the rusty wire netting on the fringe of the larch planting when a tussock started shaking, disturbing piled beech leaves and dead larch needles. Curious, but unafraid, he watched the tussock, with ears pricked forward and nostrils sifting the still, tangy air. Presently a matted ball rolled clear, trailing lengths of grass, and leaving a hollow of pressed leaves in the heart of the tussock. The ball flattened slowly, and faint snufflings came from it. Then it shook, and a small, pig-like head appeared. Nostrils sneezed gleet and eyes ungummed. The hedgehog was awake.

The hedgehog sniffed in an arc and scratched dirt from his ears with his hindfeet. Ripples passed up Bounce's gullet and he started chewing cud. The hedgehog inched towards him, trailing grass and beech leaves, then turned back to the netting to rub his face against a moss-scummed post. While he was rubbing a magpie *chuck-ucked* from a low beech branch, and Bounce, keeping his eyes on the hedgehog, waggled his ears to listen to the bird.

The magpie dipped from his perch and pitched near the netting, with tail fanned to a spear and blue wings flicking. After raising neck feathers at Bounce he swaggered up to the hedgehog, jerking his tail. Breasting the ground, and with his black head turned sideways, he tried to stab the hedgehog's eyes with his beak. But he was baulked by brow quills suddenly lowered, and danced back with wings raised and tail sweeping leaves.

Chik. Chik. Chik. Chik. He was long-necking, voicing his annoyance. Drowsy, knowing only that he was threatened, the hedgehog crouched half-coiled, still as a carving. *Chik. Chik.* The feathers on the magpie's head were rising. He was ignoring the buck, who was sitting high, watching. *Chik. Chik.* He was standing wide. *Chock-tlick!* He side-stepped nearer, with beak presented low and wings held ready for flight. Warily, he placed one foot on the pincushion. There was no response. With great savagery he began to pluck barbs from the hedgehog's hide, screwing and pulling with his beak. The hedgehog wriggled and snuffled. When sixteen quills lay at the magpie's feet, he bored head-down through the netting, tumbled into a ditch, and crawled under a canopy of shed larch branches.

The magpie, upending to poke through the screen, realised he was defeated, so he flicked to a post and, with head low, peered boldly at Bounce with his bright, dark eye. He flew down and skipped towards him, flirting his tail. Bounce, chewing cud, followed him with his eyes as he side-stepped past his flank, but was completely caught off guard when the magpie whisked up to his rear and pulled a beakful of white fur from his flag. Amazed and furious he leaped from his couch and struck out with a forehoof. But the magpie, skipping clear of the hoof-stroke, flew chuckling to a beech branch, where he held the white tuft under a foot while he teased it to threads with his beak.

White hairs drifted down from the beech tree. Bounce, angered by the magpie and irked by peeling velvet, stamped beside the netting and ripped rotten wood from a post with his prongs. Then a twig snapped in Braeburn and he was alert and taut on the instant, standing with head high and ears forward, seeking the cause of the sound.

Hearing no repetition, he back-tracked slowly through the larches, keeping his ears set forward, and walked cat-footed along the inside of the netting. The *spinking* of shilfas, and a cock pheasant sprinting forward, told of an enemy in the wood. Bounce stepped warily, freezing after each four paces, with chin level and nostrils open. He was trying to find the twig-snapper with his nose. And, presently, faint and elusive on the treacherous eddies of air, he found the scent of man! He trembled; and the spring came into his legs. His flag spread and twitched. Now he knew! Without waiting for further snap to twigs, he turned in his tracks, leaped lightly over the netting, and trotted silently away.

Suddenly, the magpie *shuggied* in the beech and rose vertically from his perch with flick and spread of tail; he had just seen the man in the wood. When Bounce ceased stamping and stabbing the man knew that twig-snap had alerted the deer; he also guessed that wind flaffs in the larches might be playing him false. When the magpie yattered he knew that every second counted. The deer might be making a stealthy withdrawal. So he hurried forward, ducking under low, foiling larch branches, and cleared the smother in time to see the buck loping under beeches towards the open.

Three shots from the ·22 automatic, fired from kneeling position, sent the cushats crashing from the larches and the cock pheasant rocketing over the wood. Two fields away, Fraser of Stane Farm was stooping in front of a spluttering tractor, moving peewit eggs out of the way of harrows. When rifle fire rattled in Braeburn he rose and started running towards the wood.

Two bullets whined high over Bounce's head; the third scruffed the skin of his neck. He felt the sting of it almost in the same moment as he heard the slap of the rifle. Terrified, he breinged from the beeches, barking four times; then he was away across the cornfield, travelling fast and mute in tremendous bounds.

Peewits trailed from nests in his path and pitched clear to preen feathers: others, tap-dancing for worms, swung up in twisting flight and tossed screaming about his head. Fraser, seeing the deer in full flight, cursed aloud, and ran faster in a fury. Like his neighbours, he never shot at roe. Bounce, viewing the man, held away to the bottom of the field, and did not turn along the next hedge for Glencryan because he was afraid of the tractor ticking over near the wood. Sailing gracefully over the hedge, he ran the furrows in the next field, startling rooks with half-filled food pouches, and galloped past staring cattle beasts towards the Wood-of-no-name.

But men were there, and in the glen across the road, felling trees and lopping branches. Bounce crossed the road out of gunshot of the wood, and plunged downhill to the burn. A weasel, peering from a burrow where he had just killed a field mouse, spat and nickered when he was showered with leaves and pebbles, then whipped back just in time to elude the gouging hooves of the deer. In the scrub across the burn, near Fin-me-oot cottage, Bounce halted to blow. His tongue was showing. Seeing rabbits ambling quietly in the scrub, he knew that no peril lurked, so he scraped a hollow with his forehooves and kneed down to rest.

The voices of the men in the glen came loud to his ears, so he did not stir till they had finished work for the day. Voles were running in the scrub, biting grass stalks and each other, and twice, while the sun was yet bright, a big tawny owl flew from his roost in a burn-side syca-more and clutched one in his claws. An hour before sun-set Bounce rose and approached the sycamore, watched by the grave, dark eyes of the owl. The owl inflated his throat, crooned, and flew away when Bounce started stabbing the trunk and scaling off curled bark with his prongs. Ladybird beetles, spiders and a queen wasp fell with bark on his withers. Beetles and spiders crawled and fell among leaves; the wasp quivered her wings and flew to the roots of a fallen tree, where she died in the frost of the night.

Bounce was still rubbing vigorously when he heard the tinkle of a tiny bell, followed by a cry that sent up his ears and spun him round with flag blossoming full and white.

Whee-yoo: whee-yoo: whee-yoo!

It was the call of a doe to fawns, unremembered by Bounce, yet recognised instantly. But the doe wearing the collar and hanging bell was not calling fawns; she was calling Bounce! She was his sister, though neither could know it—Sanshach the saucy one; Patrick MacPherson's foundling—slim, gleg, and well-fed, and redder than Bounce. She had almost shed her coat of winter grey and her throat flashes had vanished. It is doubtful if he remembered her, for he had not visited Fin-me-oot since the autumn and Sanshach seldom wandered to the Glencryan side of the burn.

Bounce stepped mincingly to meet her, then shied away, for she had man and dog smell on her, and he was suspicious of the bell. When she ran to him, he trotted away ahead of her—through the scrub, into the open, and up to the leafing thorn hedge flanking the orchard. Dog smell there sent him running along the hedge, but not before Patrick had spied him, with Sanshach chasing. Patrick watched them running and circling in the field till they were lost in the gathering dusk, then, calling in his dog, he settled with a pipe in his rocking chair to reflect on what he had seen.

During the night Sanshach traipsed after Bounce, trying to head him or persuade him to stand for her; but he would not let her touch him. Buck and doe though they were, and sib, the collar and bell made him nervous, and his eyes could not quickly overcome the doubts born of his scent and hearing. Sanshach was perplexed, but persisted in herding him. Yet, when the sun rose, and he trotted to harbour in Glencryan, she made no attempt to follow. She turned away and cantered home to the orchard. Though she ranged freely at night, unrestricted by the man who had saved her life, she had never spent the daylight away from the cottage, where she had roof cover when the days were wet.

At midday, Patrick called her. And when she came to him he fussed her, and scratched her ears, and removed the collar from her neck. Fond though he was of her, he had never tried to keep her from her own, and having seen her with the buck he guessed she might go to him, just as he shrewdly surmised that her alien trappings might keep the buck from accepting her.

Bounce did not meet Sanshach again till opening catkins had blurred the clean twig tracery of the Glencryan beeches. By then his antlers were clean and hard, ridged and pearled to his ivory top tines, and weathered to the dark colour of pine bark. His back tines, precociously grown, were white and smooth and no longer than the tusks of foxes. A grass blade could not have passed between the burred edges of the coronets on his skull.

He was browsing along the north fence of Glencryan, on a night of full moon, biting at pink flowers of ragged robin and stitchwort clusters that reached to his chin, when he heard Sanshach in the cornfield. Before wheeling to greet her, he thrashed fence wires and saugh bushes with his nine-inch dags, and this time he allowed her to approach without fuss. She came without hesitation, and touched his face and neck with her muzzle. She breathed the fawn-call in his ears. In response, Bounce scraped the fur of her neck with his antlers, and raked playfully at her flank. And, when he danced head-tossing away, she followed him at once into the moonlight and shadow of the wood.

At the fox den by the burn they stopped to stamp fore-hooves. Fox smell came rank from the hole under the boulder, where a vixen was lying with five woolly cubs which she had carried there in her jaws two days before. Three dead rats lay at the den mouth, beside the wings of a curlew and the whiskered head of a hare. Bounce shook his head, butted playfully at the doe, and shied away from the den. Ever since Dryflatts he had made threat display at the scent or sight of fox.

In the beechwood Bodach, the badger, was scooping young rabbits, wool and grass from a hole which he had dug through the deep, wet mould. His mate, crouched beside him, was biting the rabbits as they were tossed at her feet. Bodach had found the doe rabbit's nursery burrow after Bounce entered the wood, but instead of digging along the tunnel from the entrance he had worked down to the nest from a point directly above. Curious, the deer minced close behind the badgers. Bodach grunted without anger, and went on with his digging. When six young rabbits lay dead on the leaves, the badgers snatched them up in their jaws and carried them to the shadow of a beech tree where they crouched to eat them.

The deer pulled catkins and sheathed buds from low-spreading beech branches, then lay down near the nest of the owls to rest and cud. Their chewing was heard by the hen owl on the nest, where she was heaving on three squirming owlets. The moon glinted on jet muzzles each time the deer moved their heads. Bounce lent his ears to the near sounds of the night—the squeak and patter of voles in the blaeberries, the flutter of wings shaken in sleep, the cheetering of the owlets when the hen rose to change position on the nest. Twice, while the roe cudded, One Eye arrived with voles, and they hearkened to the wailing of him as he flashed overhead on noiseless wings with the prey in his beak.

Day break came grey with misted rain, and Sanshach left the wood. Bounce followed her along the hedge, snatching leafing twigs of thorn and reaching down for brooklime and speedwell growing in the ditch. Rabbits were out, nibbling corn blades silvered with rain. At the far end of the wood a cock pheasant was *took-tooking* as he paraded on the cornfield edge. He ran twenty paces at the approach of the deer, then crowed and beat his wings in drumming display, standing straight and tall with puffed-out chest. It was then Bounce and Sanshach saw the switch-horn and his herd among the birches, cropping blaeberries and bleached tussocks of twitch.

Six deer stood taut with ears erect when they found fox smell suddenly on the wind, and in a moment a big dog fox came trotting along the inside of the fence, with wet legs and sleeked brush and two rats in his jaws. He was snaking round wet tussocks and scrub to keep his flank fur dry. The switch-horn stamped and shook water from birch twigs, while Bounce thrashed wild parsley and fence wires with his prongs; but the fox trotted on, slit-eyed and unsnarling, without trick or display. His two rats made nine killed by him in the Stane Farm stackyard since the previous dusk.

Afterwards, Sanshach paunched full on grass and unfolding thorn leaves, but would not be herded back into the wood. Each time Bounce tried to head her, she eluded him and frisked nearer the Stane Farm lane. At last, with a shake of her head, she left him and cantered unhesitatingly to the farm. Bounce, watching from screening aspens in the ditch, trembled and stamped at the spectacle of a roe doe running straight to two men and a black-and-white collie, with the wind on her face and the menace in full view. For nerve-wracking seconds he stood at gaze, with flag spreading full in uncertainty, but when the dog danced round Sanshach, barking, he wheeled in his tracks and bounded headlong into the wood.

Nightly, after that, Sanshach came to the wood, her coat tawny-red in the sunset glare, and often she was grazing on young grass and clover before Bounce came from harbour. Soon the woods and hedgerows were green, and they found all their feeding on the wood-edge and in the surrounding fields; but, though they fed and cudded and played together from dusk till dawn, Sanshach always returned to the orchard in the morning. When three tawny owlets were wing-flapping in pine branches, and the beech leaves quivered pellucid in sunlight, she began to linger in Glencryan till mid-morning or noon. Sometimes Bounce wandered with her to Fin-me-oot in the night, to nibble currant buds and apple blossom; but he would not lie in the unchancy place by day. And Patrick, seeing them, marvelled that his doe should be so stubbornly attached to her alien home.

When the young corn was tall enough to hide nesting peewits, and the oak leaves were greening, Bounce began to harbour out in the heather during daylight, often lying on his side with legs outstretched if the sun was warm. On wet days he returned to the wood. Grouse had their chicks in the heather before he rubbed off the last matted grey hair from his shoulders against gnurly birches on the moor; then he was sleek and foxy-red like Sanshach, and the new hair silked softly in the sun.

They were frisking together on a dry stretch of young, leafy heather, within sight of the wood, when they heard the faint crack of a rifle in the Wood-of-no-name. For a moment they stood with ears up, testing the wind with their noses. But the morning sun was warm. Flies made them twitch their ears. They forgot, and resumed their frolics, chasing each other in crazy circles and figures of eight. On the heather fringe was a grassy hummock, with a hollow on top, in which a curlew was sitting on four green, pear-shaped eggs. Each time the deer approached the hummock the curlew ran from her nest with lifted wings and open beak, and drove them off. Bounce yielded ground without threat, embarrassed by the curlew's wings striking his legs.

They played closer and closer to a slope where bracken grew tall among crowded birches and, suddenly, the doe halted rigid and upright in her tracks, listening. Instantly, Bounce copied her pose, and heard. From the bracken slope came a cry that no roe could possibly mistake. . . .

Eep-eep. Eep. Nee-eep.

Sanshach inched forward, stamping at each second step, knowing she was hearing the distress cry of a fawn. Bounce minced at her flank, with the spring in his knee. His slim neck was rigid. When they reached the bracken fringe the cry was repeated. *Eep-eep: nee-ee-eep.* Sanshach shouldered her way warily through the bracken, with only head showing, and Bounce in her slots. And presently they saw him, on a dry hummock in the bracken, with muzzle resting on up-gathered hind legs and long, down-sweeping lashes shielding his violet eyes from the sun.

Since the first pallor of daybreak he had lain there, unmoving, without flicker of eye, twitch of ear, or tremor of flank, or the faintest hunger-cry. But his mother, absent since the middle of the night, was long in coming. He had panted to thirst and hunger in the increasing heat of the sun. Then, when the flies came out, whining or buzzing or rasping according to their breed, he had wagged ears and wrinkled nostrils under their tormenting assault. And the movements, forced upon him by torment, had at last released him from the iron grip of instinct.

Eep-eep.

His coat was sun-silked, and he was sick with warmth. Sanshach waggled her ears. Bounce stamped. The fawn called again, and soon, as if in answer to his summons, his mother appeared in the bracken. Bounce and Sanshach drew back till their faces were foiled by bracken; but the doe was not aware of them. The fawn heard her, and smelled her; then, at last, he saw her—slim of leg and neck, reddening into her full summer coat, but grey on the shoulders where winter hair still lingered.

Reddening? Yes, she was reddening; but behind her left shoulder her coat was streaked with scarlet—scarlet trickles of her own blood, her life blood; a brighter colour, sun-glinted, oozing from a bullet hole near her heart.

She came on towards her fawn, weaving, swaying, weak of leg and heavy of eye, and her drooped ears told of mortal wounds. Blow-flies were already crowding the blood-glaze behind her shoulder. She had been shot in the Wood-of-no-name, at close range, by a youth with a rifle; but when the bullet blurred the world before her eyes she had leaped away, as if unhit, and reached the heather at speed, out of his reach and beyond his tracking powers. Her last thoughts—if a roe can have thoughts—were for her little buck fawn with the snowflaked coat lying lonely in the bracken. And when she reached him she was dying.

Eep-eep! he said in greeting, and rose to nurse. The doe made a gurgling sound in her throat and turned her flank to him. He nursed eagerly, greedily, boisterously, pushing and pummelling, and almost lifting her from her feet While he nursed, her eyes glazed over. The bullet was draining away her life faster than the fawn could drain her milk. She swayed—stumbled—and fell. . . .

The fawn danced back, astonished at her behaviour, and licked milk from his blue-black muzzle. Then he muzzled her face, squeaking half in wonder and half in impatience. She licked him once, as tenderly as she had licked him when he first saw the light of day. Then her tongue drooped, gathering bracken dust and fuzz, and she lay still—very still. She would never lick him again.

Bounce relaxed and turned away through the bracken: perhaps, for him, the tragedy had no meaning. But Sanshach stepped slowly towards the fawn, mute, nervous, with her head low. She stepped jerkily round the dead doe, with her ears laid back, then reached out her muzzle to the fawn. He looked up, and tossed his baby head, without moving from the body of his mother. And when Sanshach retraced her steps slowly into the bracken he made no move to follow her.

Through the long, hot day Bounce and Sanshach couched in the heather under screening birches, while the fawn voiced his baby plaint, heedless of what ears might prick to hearken. When dusk came, blue-violet, with a soft wind, Sanshach returned to the bracken slope, and found the fawn nuzzling his mother and tapping her gently with a tiny forehoof, as if pleading with her to rise and take notice of him. Sanshach grazed round the bracken, forgetting Bounce. Cuckoos fell silent; the wild skirling of curlews died to ghost-trills. And the fawn cried in the gathering darkness.

Many times in the night Sanshach returned to him. But, though his baby heart was sore with loneliness and hunger, he did not run to her. When freshening wind brought driving rain at daybreak, he lay down beside the doe, shivering and weak. And, at mid-morning, when he was dead, Sanshach left the fern brake to join Bounce out in the heather and run with him to Glencryan.

17

AFTER MIDSUMMER, WHEN FLOWERS CLUSTER ON THE brambles and the sun kindles the fireweed to flames, the mating fever burns in the blood of roe and badger, and the love season lasts while grouse moult their claws and the corn changes from green to ripened gold.

Brock and small-antlered deer are beasts of ancient lineage. They knew the cave bear. Their bones lie in deposits older than the glaciers; one with the remains of lynx and hyena and rhinoceros. The roe and badger of modern times are little different from their forebears who roamed the forests before Britain was an island. And, to-day, they share the mystery of long-delayed birth: for the small living cell, produced by summer mating, lies dormant in doe and sow, undeveloping, till after the year's shortest day.

Bounce was pawing hoof-scrapes among the hazels, and thrashing branches with his prongs, when the mating moon's crescent was paling in the dawn. Five white-tipped fox cubs and two badger cubs were running in the wood. When One Eye pitched and hooted, Bounce back-tracked from the hazels and trotted to the north fence, where Sanshach was grazing on lush grass and clover on the cornfield edge. He wanted to fuss, but she leaped away, head-tossing, each time he hustled her, biting grass when she stopped and chewing as she ran. At the field end they saw Bodach and his mate entering the wood. In the night the badgers had played leap-frog in secret places on the moor; and before coming home they had gorged on grass, clover and rhizomes, slugs and beetles, which they found in the hedge bottoms and Stane Farm fields.

In the warm July days Bounce pawed many scrapes under oaks and hazels, and left the scuff-marks of his prongs on their stems. At dawn, he chased barking after Sanshach, and sometimes he ran with her halfway to the orchard when the sun was high.

On a morning of sky-haze and lark-song, when the year's fledged peewits were flock-flying with the old birds above pasture and foggage, he followed her to the Fin-me-oot hedge. But he would not lie up with her in the orchard. He couched near the burn, under tall, spreading limes, hidden by antler-high angelica and fragrant meadowsweet. During the close, still, sunless day he cudded and dozed, with ears tuned to water music and the bee symphony in the limes, and when woodcock were flapping in owl-flight from the glen he sought Sanshach at the orchard hedge.

They grazed and browsed at a walk to Stane Farm, and pulled aspen leaves in the lane before the house was dark. On the cornfield edge they ate eyebright, vetch tufted and yellow, sneezewort and yarrow, and tall red clover, while rabbits rustled in the corn and bats hawked above the woodside trees. The faint screaming of swifts drew down the darkening sky where the eagle star, Altair, flickered. Suddenly, Bounce threw up his head, and faced the wood with both ears forward.

Wa-ap; wa-ap; wa-a-ap!

The cries came from the beechwood, near the badgers' den. Bounce shook his head and stamped smartly with a foot. He knew the meaning of the tushkarue: many little tods were barking in the wood. Walking stiff-necked to the fence, he leaped lightly into the wood, and thrashed in the birches till leaves fell at his feet and the twigs were frayed by his prongs. Then he stood upright, pulling and chewing leaves. The confused fox chorus continued, and soon the curlews were calling. Bounce's curiosity was aroused, and in a moment he was moving stealthily towards the beechwood; but, if curiosity was driving him to seek explanations, it was the rut-fire that sent him in with the spring in his knees and anger in his heart.

On the edge of the beechwood he moved warily in the thickets. The rank taint of fox lay heavy on the air; that was his first certain information. The smell of them stank in his nostrils. And, presently, he picked out the whole clanjamfrie, five of them, weaving about on the leaf carpet among the buirdly beech boles—dark, moving smudges in the gloom of the wood. At first, he could not make out the cause of the excitement. Then he found it with eyes and nose in a leafy hollow under wide-spreading beech branches. The smell of him was almost hidden by the reek of fox; but there was no mistaking the black and white face. Bodach, the badger, was being baited by foxes.

Bounce was at a loss. He could not understand that the foxes wanted the rabbit which Bodach was stoically eating in the hollow under the beech. The badger had brought it there, snare and all, from the beech fringe of Braeburn, to devour under cover, and he was not being stampeded into parting with it by any number of callow foxes snarling in his ears. He knew the young tods were bluffing, and hoping for leavings. When he had eaten his fill he would scatter them with teeth and claws that would not be bluffing. But, while he was still far from sated, the vixen appeared, with eyes slitted, brush tucked in, and nothing more than saliva in her mouth.

She came flat-eared and snarling. Perhaps she thought that Bodach had taken the rabbit from her cubs; or that he had been molesting them. Whatever she thought, she rushed at him, snarling in his face and biting at his scut.

Bodach wanted to keep his teeth in his rabbit, but it meant leaving his tag of a tail at the mercy of the vixen. His thick hide he did not mind about; but he was sensitive about his scut. So he whipped round, grunting like a rooting hog, to show the bitch fox the colour of his teeth. She noted, and drew back—stiff-legged, with birses up, and her cubs hustling her from behind. She had no stomach for a teeth-to-teeth girning match with a badger, so long as there was no threat to her cubs. She was prepared to bide her time.

But, while she waited, a dark shape launched from a thicket. It approached in tremendous bounds, and the vixen did not pause to wonder why a roebuck should come at her so murderously without provocation. Bounce struck out with a forehoof as she turned. The blow would have split her skull if it had made solid contact; instead, it took her on the side of the face, gouging an eye, splitting her lip and breaking a tusk. Like a snake, she eluded the following antler thrust that would have pinned her to the ground, and raced silently for cover. Her cubs scattered yelping, with brushes curled between hindlegs under their bellies. And, when the patter of their feet died away, the wood was silent.

Bounce stabbed the beech trunk, and churned leaves with his hooves. Bodach sniffed in an arc, licked his scut, and returned to his rabbit. He was crunching thigh bones, and clawing gut from his face, when Sanshach ambled into the beechwood in search of Bounce, and he did not look up when they wandered away, browsing leaves from low beech branches as they walked.

The night was moonless, and the deer left the wood to cud in the heather. At break of day they saw the Glencryan dog fox skulking home with dew-soaked brush and a Light Sussex pullet in his jaws; he had killed the bird at Stane Farm, and left seven others without heads under the stackyard hedge. Rain in the early afternoon drove them into the wood, but men's voices near the fox den three hours later sent them back to the moor, where they lay till nightfall. Next morning the sun rose red and frayed of edge in the mists, and they lingered in the farm lane to feel its warmth before entering the wood near the fox den at the burn.

They did not drink, for they had fed wet in the night, but Bounce trampled knee-deep in the burn to pull leafed stalks of comfrey from the clumps on the bank. He struck the water with a forehoof as he browsed, to splash clegs from his belly, and wagged ears against vicious flies. Near him a dipper was walking the bottom of a shallow pool, oaring with its wings, seeking caddis grubs on the gravel. The grubs were crawling on the burn bed, trailing body-sheathing tubes of grass-stalks and rush fragments, lined with silk woven from strands produced in their mouths. When the dipper surfaced, and splashed to a flat stone with a beakful of green caddis-cases, Bounce shied away and leaped out to join Sanshach on the bank.

Coal heads were catching caddis flies in the bushes overhanging the water, and flying with them to nests among the rushes in the woodside ditch. Bounce minced to the fox den, with Sanshach muzzling his flank, and when he stopped to stamp a hoof she thrust skittishly ahead. *Click-ang!* Sanshach leaped high, screaming like a wounded hare. She had sprung with a forefoot one of the gins set in the open near the den for the feet of foxes.

Bounce crashed through bushes into the water, sending coal heads and tam tits whirring out in alarm. He clambered out on the opposite bank, crackling in the brushwood, and bounded to the cornfield fence with the doe's screams in his ears. Crows yarred and flapped high on black wings; cushats flashed from the oaks in downswept flight; One Eye, on his perch, swivelled his big head round on stretched neck and *wee-wicked* with throat pouch gulping.

On the field edge Bounce stood rigid, with flag twitching, till the crying of Sanshach sobbed to a wail, then silence. Then the spring came to his knee, and a glitter to his eyes, and he sailed over the fence to seek her in the wood.

She had uprooted the peg in her struggles, and was lying on the bank with the gin clamped to her left foreleg and spittle on her face. The steel teeth gripping the bone were splattered with blood. Her flanks were heaving; leaf fuzz and dirt clung to her hanging tongue. At sight of Bounce she kicked to her feet and hirpled painfully towards him, dragging the trapped leg, with the chain rattling and snagging in the grass. Bounce circled her, with ears laid back. Almost savagely, he prodded her flank. This was something beyond his understanding.

Her first panic over, Sanshach staggered after him, mute. Time after time the chain caught in roots or brushwood or blaeberry clump as she followed him through the wood; but, though she plunged and kicked and fell in renewal of panic, she did not cry. The crows pitched, and One Eye slept, and the cushats flapped back to the oaks. And Sanshach paused, with ears erect, seeking direction with her eyes. In her extremity she was orientating herself for home—for the orchard, and Patrick, where there was no fear.

So she turned aside and dragged heavily towards the burn. Bounce tried to force her about, gently at first, then brusquely; but she fought him off, and limped, and staggered, and stumbled to the water. She went in where the ground was level, and clanked across slowly, but the opposite bank was high and heavy with growth and she was forced to struggle downstream, slipping and lurching, to seek a way out. Finding none quickly, she gave way to panic. With a mighty effort, she reared and pawed the bank with her trapped leg. Her hind-hooves gouged for a foothold. But the chain caught in a root, tugging against her as she tried to scramble up, and she was pulled back into the water, on to her back, with three legs flailing.

Above her, on the high bank, Bounce thrashed in willows and briars, and ripped through valerian and hog-weed with his prongs. Hollow stems snapped, and briar petals eddied down to the water where Sanshach was lying. She fought on to her side, and panted, holding her head clear of the dark water running swift under the bank. Many times her head sagged, and she threw up, snorting, when the water rushed in her mouth. But at last she was exhausted, and her struggles weakened, and she drowned kicking feebly where pink petals swirled.

The dark water sleeked the coat of Sanshach and the foam frothed in rings about her neck. For two days Bounce kept tryst with her, resting in the bank tangles by day and grazing along the woodside fence at dusk and dawn. When an old man came on the third day, searching for a lost doe in Glencryan, he stamped petulantly and withdrew to a thicket. The man wandered in the wood, calling *Sanshach! Sanshach!* And at last he found the drowned thing in the water. And after he had splashed out to her, and stroked her, and said: "Sanshach, my *caileag*! Poor cratur!" he left for Stane Farm to ask for a spade, and came back and buried her under the hazels in Glencryan.

In the still mornings of silver dew and sun-sparkle, before the smoke from farm chimneys rose blue to become one with the sky-haze, the switch-horn barked in Glencryan. And Bounce, forgetting Sanshach, barked in reply.

On the fourth morning after her death he stalked stiff-legged through the wood, tawny-red in the leaf-filtered light, with neck stretched level and ears angled lower than his horns. The old switch was parading in a grassy clearing, dotted with hummocks from which blackcock with lyre tails had challenged in the spring; his doe was out of sight, cudding in a thicket. The yearlings, nervous of the old buck's morning tantrums, were harboured together out in the heather. The doe's fawn of the year, survivor of twins, was couched among blaeberries a little distance from her mother; her brother, long since, had ended his brief life in the belly of a fox. Bounce thrashed branches on the fringe of the clearing, and barked, and the switch-horn turned grunting to face him.

They braced back against their thighs, with forehooves pawing the mould, before launching to the assault, and met antler to antler in the middle of the clearing. At the first shock the switch almost hunkered, for Bounce was strong; but, when they circled head to head, stabbing, the old buck's unforked horns slipped through his guard, scoring his face and narrowly missing an eye. So Bounce skipped away, to circle warily round the clearing, with the switch parading stiffly on an inner ring. Again they leaped to the attack, and the old buck was shaken; but again his long dirks slipped through, jabbing Bounce on skull and coronet. And this time he bounded from the clearing, barking, with the switch running in his slots to the edge of the wood.

He was far out on the heather, near Hoolet Nest, travelling with the wind on the side of his face and his ears alert for sound, before the milk pails were clattering at Skeoch Farm. Skirting the deserted, feather-strewn gullery, he stopped to watch a black crow flapping in a gin, which had been set in an old nest by the keeper and baited with a green-dyed egg. The grouse coveys were strong on the wing, and five birds rose from a pebbly sap of water when he went to drink. After drinking, he lay down to rest in deep heather, where two coal heads were fluttering with beaks full of caterpillars.

The sun climbed hotly, and he turned his eyes from the glare. There was a bruise between coronet and eyebrow where the switch's horn had stabbed. Every six minutes he pricked his ears when a coal head whirred down to a heather clump with caterpillars. The birds had five nestlings, which had hatched from four eggs, for one egg had been double-yolked and twin chicks had wriggled from the shell. In the late afternoon Smokey Joe, the hoodie, flapped to the nest and ate all five chicks, standing with his black legs braced widely apart. He left calling *Haar!* and when the coal heads returned they pushed caterpillars into the bottom of the nest. They were still feeding grubs to the empty nest when the sun was red and Bounce rose from his knees for the evening feed.

In the fiery gold and crimson of the sunset he grazed on sheep-bitten grass near the ruin, and ate many rats' tails of plantain at the crumbling doorway. While he grazed, Smokey Joe *kwarped* harshly, taunting a white owl in the chimney. Rabbits ambled from the threshes to feed crouching on the sward. Bounce grazed beyond the gable-end while the sky was still bright and a wind eddy brought to his nostrils the scent of roe.

She was out near the heather line, paunching on moor grass, looming large in the half-light—Sona, the sprightly one, with twin fawns at foot. The fawns were tiny and knock-kneed and spotted with white, born at the peak of the rut, and only four days old. They had just nursed and were licking milk smears from each other's muzzle.

Bounce strode from the shadows, checked with ears and nose, then cantered boldly out to the doe. She looked up at his approach, but danced away when he tried to fuss. With fawns only four days old, she was not ready for dalliance, and when he ran her in a circle, with his muzzle on her withers, she stopped suddenly and butted him smartly on the ribs. He leaped away in mock fright, but came back to be dunted again. After she had butted him four times he moved cautiously to her head, lipped her muzzle, stroked her neck with his antler tips and grazed moor grass beside her.

But he was restless and fretful, chivvying her as she grazed and prodding playfully at her rump every time she lay down to rest. When she called up her fawns to nurse, he stood away, shaking his head and grazing perfunctorily. At first light, Sona put her fawns down in the heather and raced with him to Hoolet Nest, where she rubbed against the chestnut tree by the gable and fed greedily on plantain and sourock inside the ruin. By then, Bounce was less commanding, and she allowed him to scratch her flank with his prongs. But she would not run for him, and once he loped on a circuit of the steading by himself.

At sunrise, a six-pointer buck strode purposefully from the threshes beyond the greensward and viewed Bounce and Sona grazing beside the ruin. He was haughty and spring-footed, foxy-red of coat and five years old, with the scars of old fights on his face. He stamped his foot and barked. The hair of Bounce's flag stood erect at the sound, but there was no sudden blossoming of white. There was anger in him, but no fear. So he pawed the sod with a forehoof, and stepped out stiffly to meet the challenger, with head low, and neck stretched and rigid.

They met near the glassless window of Hoolet Nest, evenly matched in all but back tines. Bounce, now thirty inches tall at the shoulder, threw seventy-five pounds of tough sinew and rippling muscle into the attack, with a savagery that daunted the six-pointer at the outset. The white owl, sitting wide-eyed in the chimney, heard sudden grunts and the click of antlers. Smokey Joe flew from chestnut-crown to wall-top, to throw rubble over his shoulder and chortle sarcastic comment.

The bucks locked antlers. They pushed, then withdrew: they braced, pranced and charged again. Engaging, pushing, withdrawing and re-engaging, they slotted an acre of the green in-bye, and after eleven attacks were back at the window. Recoiling from the twelfth shock, the six-pointer skidded on a moss-scummed whin embedded in the grass; his head went up, and an antler stab in the brisket almost seated him on the window-sill. As he thrust forward to regain balance Bounce raked him on the flank, scoring two deep furrows from shoulder to hip-joint. The furrows reddened in the wake of his prongs. And, in that moment, the bleeding buck accepted defeat. He squeezed along the wall, against which Bounce was trying to pin him, and, dragging clear, bounded for the open moor. Bounce barked, but did not pursue.

Smokey Joe flapped *kraa-ing* into the chestnut, where he chuckled and stabbed his perch between his feet. Bounce scraped mortar from the wall with his antler tips, then bit and spat hairy leaves of silver-weed growing at the base. When he turned to rub against the nearest pine, eight kestrels lifted from the branches—Kree and Yellow Foot and their six fledglings of the year. The kestrels flew towards Skeoch, and a flock of pigeons, all white-barred blue in the morning sun, clattered up from the re-seeded acres on which they had been feeding. But there was no sign of Sona.

She was back on the heather line, nursing her fawns. Bounce ran to her, kicking his heels. He nuzzled her face, and licked her erect ears, and when she put her fawns down again he went to them and pressed the head of each with his chin. And the fawns cowered under the rare caress of the buck who had taken command. No other buck came to Hoolet Nest to challenge and, in the blue and yellow days of ripening corn, Bounce and Sona harboured in the heather near the ruin, and browsed on sweet raspberries along the cornfield hedge when the sun was low. Curlews grew restless in recollection of the tideways, and their coronach died on the moor. Ants flew in nuptial flight in the fading daylight, and queens, falling on the backs of the deer, were crushed when they rubbed against trees. Others dropped to earth, where they shed their wings before crawling away to found new colonies, and perhaps survive beyond the life-span of a roe.

The fawns of Sona, primsie when tired but full of wild cantrips at wakening, were heavily snowflaked with white after the spots had faded on May-born roe in Dryflatts and Glencryan. But they were now strong on foot, and fleet, and tasted thorn leaves and clover while Bounce and Sona were browsing on the cornfield edge.

In the chill pallor of an August dawn, the herd was feeding on raspberries and bramble leaves when they heard a greater rustling in the wind-stirred corn. The doe halted, with the fawns at her side. Bounce, fronting the herd, pricked his ears, then edged into the wind to find the smell of badger. The badger was rolling in the corn, ridding himself of vengeful wasps which were crawling on his coat and shooting needles of flame into his snout because he had rooted out their bike in the hedgebottom and eaten the grubs. Brock stopped rolling to grunt without malice at the deer, and the roe, after stamping, moved on.

Five men coming from Skeoch Farm with guns, when cloud shadows were racing over the sunlit heather, put the herd on foot; but no shot was fired at the fleeing deer. Bounce, cantering ahead of the trio, heard the wing-whir and tinkle of hurtling grouse, followed by gunfire and the shouts of men. Without looking back, he led his little herd

right off the heather to the gorse brake he had found
during the drives for foxes in the spring.

They lay in the brake, remote and sun-silked, while bees
droned in the yellow gorse blooms and grouse fell to gunfire on the moor. The fawns panted, hollow-cheeked, and
moved into the shade of bushes. Seed pods were exploding
on the gorse, and when the seeds fell to the ground they
were gathered and carried away by ants. From the
heather came hares, goggle-eyed, with ears low, to skulk
in the brake. Every two minutes a tam tit flitted to a
gorse spike with caterpillars for fledged chicks crammed
in a feather-lined nest. The roe cudded, and slept, till the
men left the moor; then they drank thirstily from a spring-
fed pool and loped back to Hoolet Nest.

But from that day they were frequently put on foot
from their lairs, when men came from Skeoch to shoot on
the moor. The rain came, and for four mornings there was
no sunrise. Buck and doe were nervous, and irked by wet
harbours. So one morning, with the wind driving rain
on his muzzle, Bounce led his herd across the drenched
heather to the familiar runways and sheltering thickets
of Glencryan.

18

WHEN THE STOOKS WERE CLEARED FROM THE STANE
Farm fields, and the new furrows glinted in the
sun, Bounce and Sona trysted at dawn on the hillocky
clearing where blackcock in crimson wattles had displayed
and postured in the spring.

The centre of their mating ring was an embedded,
lichened boulder, with green moss stars on top and a
squat birch seedling rooted to the dark soil in a cleft. On
the first morning, Bounce made three circuits of the
boulder, coaxed round by Sona who danced sideways
ahead of him and kept her muzzle just out of reach of his
own; then he broke off the game, and wandered in the
wood, and would not be lured or hustled back to the
ring. When she butted him with her head he chased her
half-heartedly through the trees; but when she returned
to the ring, and stood watching him with head high and
flag twitching, he bit off a birch spray and bounded away
to his lair twirling it in his lips.

The following morning she fussed and capered as she
led him to the clearing, and this time he needed no
persuasion to run. He drove her nine times round the
hoof-slotted ring, muzzling her rump and prodding com-
mandingly at her flag. Sometimes she would bound
suddenly ahead, and slow to a walk to pull feather tufts
of purple grass, but when Bounce caught up she was forced
to run on with the bite in her mouth.

They played the racing game on five successive mornings, while One Eye *wee-wicked* himself to sleep on his pine

roost and the fawns capered in the birch thickets awaiting
their return. During the brief honeymoon Bounce did not
bark or posture, nor stalk stiff-legged in challenge. Nor
did the switch-horn appear near the clearing, although
he was harboured in the wood with his herd and could
hear Bounce thrashing birch scroggs with his antlers. For
the switch-horn the jealousies of the rut were over. At
sunset, when two does and followers went out to feed, they
mixed freely till Bounce and the switch arrived in the
gloaming; then the herds split, and grazed away from
each other in the gathering darkness. But there was no
stamping, or barking, or threat display from the master
bucks.

For some days after they had deserted the ring Bounce
went to harbour with Sona in the morning. But one night,
when the stars were bright and the east wind breathed
threat of frost, he wandered far out on the moor, and
when daylight came, windless and misted, he was couched
alone in a birch grove on the heather fringe, two miles
from Glencryan. Smokey Joe was in the grove, eating a
magpie which had dropped dead among the birches after
being shot while stealing eggs in the Stane Farm stackyard. Joe always moved to the birch grove when grouse
were being shot on the moor.

Roebuck and hoodie shared the birch grove till the
berries were ripe on the brambles, and Bounce always
pricked his ears when the crow croaked or flew yarring
away. Joe fed on dead rabbits and sheep and barries, and
voles which he caught in the thicket, squeezing their
necks with his pick-axe beak. When he pitched at dusk,
ruffling his black wings and pecking pin-head dust from
between the scales of his toes, Bounce wandered out to
strange fields and roadside hedgerows to eat clover and
grass, thorn leaves and crimsoning haws, and the waxy-
vermilion berries of the rowan. In the early part of the

night he browsed at a slow walk, rarely halting to pull more than a few mouthfuls in any one place, but when the rowan clusters were out of reach he reared, forehooves to chest, and sought with his lips for the elusive berries.

One morning, with the moon clear and full, and the grass crickling with frost, he wandered into a strange wood and followed a mouldy pathway that wound and dipped between high, flanking rhododendrons. Overhead, the branches of beech and elm and sycamore formed close canopy, through which the moonlight shafted to chequer and bar and mottle the dark pathway below. Bounce moved cat-footed on the layered leaves, his nose savouring the heavy earth-smell, the tang of pines, the odour of rhododendrons and frosted bracken. The path led to a wrought-iron gate, in a four-foot wall topped with flat stones and mossy saxifrage. Bounce leaped the wall on to a well-kept lawn, and walked mincingly across the springy turf to where twin yews grew beside a sundial.

The yews were dark and closely branched, and their hearts were a dusty mass of dead twigs and withered needles, where shilfa and blackbird nested in summer and found shelter in the long winter nights. Five birds whirred out cheeping from the first yew when Bounce scored the vertical stems with his antler tips; from the second a cock pheasant burst out with hanging tail and an uproar of wings. He rose vertically, with whir and tinkle, scattering droppings, and rocketed over the high trees on the wood edge. His wild flight and alarmed crowing put up the cushats from oak and chestnut, and they were sweeping overhead on whistling wings before he crashed, *cu-cupping*, in the heart of the wood. Bounce, momentarily startled by the noise, bounded to the thick shrubbery that hid the wood-edge rabbit-netting, and stood taut and quivering —listening. The silence was hissing long in his ears before he stepped back into the open.

He prowled about the lawn and shrubberies for more than an hour afterwards, lipping perfunctorily at leaf and twig as he walked. Near the rabbit netting he found many little honey-coloured toadstools which he ate with obvious relish; the bitter, purple berries of the dogwood he spat out with equally obvious distaste. He sniffed, without biting, at the ferny foliage of southernwood, then shied away snorting and shaking his head. Most to his liking were the buddleias, and he ate leaves and twigs, and the long flower spikes on which peacock and tortoise-shell butterflies gathered by day. But he found much for his paunch in the herbaecous border, which stretched the full length of the lawn, in the shelter of the high garden wall.

There he bit columbine and aster and lupin, shrivelled larkspur and woody stems of nemesia; then he found a bed of wallflowers, ready for transplanting. After snipping the heads off many wallflowers he cantered back to the lawn. Near one of the yews he prepared his couch, scraping with a forehoof on the frosting grass till he skinned and cut the flawless surface. When the sun was high, and the cranreuch lying lightly on grass and leaf, he returned to the border, and rested in the thick cover, in upright posture, with pink and yellow lupins screening his face. Flies and bees crawled on the flowers when the sun cleared the hoar. Bounce felt the warmth as his hair silked and his eyelids drooped. He turned muzzle to flank and dozed.

The *click* of the gate in the four-foot wall brought him to the alert, but not to his feet; he had heard, and was seeing, before it swung open on its creaking hinges. Three gardeners with rakes and hoes walked through, followed by a boy and two white West Highland terriers. The dogs found him at once with their noses and, break-ing way from the boy, they crashed into the border and put him on foot. Unafraid of two such small dogs Bounce faced them resolutely for a moment, with head down and antlers forward; but the nearness of men and boy unnerved him and he soon yielded ground, seeking an exit.

The gate was his way in. It had to be his way out. And he knew it. But the road to the gate was barred. There was only one line of retreat, so he bounded through tall delphiniums and lilies and Michaelmas daisies to the far end of the border, with the terriers running the path alongside, trying to head him. At the end of the border he turned sharp left across the lawn into the shrubbery and halted to find his bearings.

The terriers raced up to within ten feet of him, but he held them off by lowering his head and stamping with a foot. The threat posture had meaning for them, and they bellied down barking. Three men and a boy were moving up slowly behind them, in line abreast, brandishing hoes and rakes held level at arms' length. Each was shouting instructions to the others. They had some wild, crazy idea of cornering him and clouting him.

Bounce broke for the rabbit-netting when they were twenty yards away, but the barrier was more than six feet high, and he was hampered in the shrubbery. Branches clawed him down as he jumped, and he hit the top with his knees and fell heavily backwards. The fall knocked the breath from him, but he was on his feet as his lungs filled, gasping and on the verge of total panic. Then, almost at once, he had no urge to panic. The glitter came into his eyes and the fire to his blood; and when a roebuck's blood runs hot with rage—hot enough to burn up fear for a fleeting moment—he can be as dangerous and unpredictable as a three-year-old Ayrshire bull.

Rearing and hog-grunting he took the offensive. He rushed at one dog, then the other, with forelegs flailing, and they broke away to escape his knife-edged hooves. The advancing line halted, amazed, when he broke cover. The terriers came in again on a converging attack, but this time they danced and barked well out of reach, and Bounce ignored them. He saw only the men. He knew he had to go through them. He knew he was going through them. And, suddenly, three men and a boy knew it too.

With his nose pointed at the gate Bounce rushed forward—straight, true and reckless of danger. Hoes and rakes were dropped as the men jumped clear of the breaking buck. The boy, running the wrong way, trod on the teeth of a rake. The shaft came up and hit him, and he stumbled almost in Bounce's path. Men shouted but Bounce did not swerve. The boy, rolling flat on his face, pushed the rake away. The shaft, coming up, caught Bounce as he leaped to miss the boy and threw him. He came down heavily, in a fankle of legs, and as he sprackled to his feet a man threw a hoe at him, spear fashion. The blade cut his shoulder but did not stop him and, in a moment, he was up and away, bounding for the gate in the wall. He went over it high and effortlessly, and leaped from the touchdown straight into the nearest bushes. The gardeners, shaken, listened to the crashing of him in the laurels and rhododendrons then gathered to compare amazements.

Bounce did not slacken pace till he had left three paths and a little glen of Norway spruces between him and the garden. When he halted in a clearing among oak trees his tongue was showing. He could hear the terriers rioting far back, but knew he had lost them in the wood. The wound on his shoulder was smarting, and he reached round to nose it and touch it with his tongue. The hair was already sticky and quilled with drying blood. Suddenly he threw himself down and rolled on the oak-leaf carpet. The sticky blood gathered mould-dust and fuzz.

Afterwards he rested in upright position, and when he left the wound was crusted and insulated against the flies.

He took the wrong path from the wood, and came out through brashed spruce poles into a small meadow overgrown with ragwort. Rooks were pushing under baked dung pats with their beaks, seeking worms in the moist warmth below. Partridges, scraping and dust-bathing in the dry, crumbly soil of moleheaps, *chooked* without fear when they saw the buck striding through the ragwort. Bounce hustled the rooks, making them flap and dance away, cawing in protest, then trotted to the burn at the bottom of the meadow. The slope ahead was a blaes ridge topped with fireweed, and he breasted it at a run to see what lay ahead.

But the fireweed reached higher than his antler tips and he had to push through the dense, brittle growth to get a view. Smoke was rising from a spinney on his left where a cottage was hidden by the trees. To his right the ground stretched level to the heather line on the horizon—sour, undrained acres of coarse grass and twitch and bents and mossy hillocks where redshank and curlew and wheatear nested in summer. Bounce loped down the slope, and turned right, heading for the heather. And met the billy goat in a hollow. . . .

The billy goat was black-and-white, with a six-inch beard, eyes like jewels, and short, back-curving horns. He was on a thirty-foot rope tether, frayed and bleached by weathering. He was kept by a farmer who believed that goats prevented abortion in dairy cows. Bounce, savouring the heavy stench of him, cast wide to avoid him. But the billy was morose, lonely, and hot with the fever of the rut. He whistled in challenge, then lunged in a rage to the end of his tether. It snapped three feet from the holding peg, and he was free. He whistled again. And when Bounce stopped to look back he saw the billy charging after him, trailing twenty-seven feet of rotting rope attached to the leather collar on his neck.

Bounce had no urge to quarrel with the evil-smelling beast; but he was thrawn with recent anger, and the threat of assault rekindled the dangerous fire that had driven him to face Man earlier that morning. So, when the goat pranced up, fast and nimble, he postured to receive him, with neck stiff, head down, and antlers set to engage.

The clash, when it came, caught both roe and goat unprepared, for each was a stranger to the other's duelling code. While the goat reared to butt downwards with his head, Bounce arched his back, bucked, and stabbed out and upwards with his antlers; there was no solid impact of skulls, or fencing with headpoints. Instead of meeting another head and off-curving horns the billy's skull came down hard on Bounce's antler tips. The blow staggered the deer almost to his knees and sent waves of pain through his coronets; the billy lost hair from his forehead and was gashed dangerously near his eye. Momentarily daunted, they recoiled. Then Bounce curved his back, pawed the ground, grunted, and leaped to the attack a second time. The goat reared as he charged, dunted downwards as before, and again felt the antler stabs on the flat of his skull.

Four times they met, savagely, with a shock that jarred Bounce's spine. The headaches were to the deer, but it was the goat who had the wounds. Blood trickled into his jewel eyes, all of it his own. When he struck down for the fifth time he made no contact for Bounce, side-stepping, had lunged past his guard. The antler dirked him in the throat, ripped clear, and raked the hair of his neck. Bounce bored in, thrusting with all the power of his wiry hindquarters. The antler gouged on, slipped under the goat's collar, and they were locked.

Each felt, and fought against, the hold. They danced round, grunting and pushing and straining, tearing the ground with their hooves; but they could not disengage. Bounce raked and stabbed with the locked antler, while the billy, edging round, struck sideways with his head. When he tried to lower his head to hook with his horns he was pulled up by the stranglehold of the collar. The position was favouring Bounce. The goat began to panic. Suddenly, he danced backwards, pulling hard on the collar and almost lifting Bounce off the ground. Bounced lunged forward, but the weight was off his forelegs and the billy's head went up. The collar strained, but did not break. When the break came it was Bounce's forward tine that snapped. The antler slipped clear and they were free.

The goat fled then, with his neck dripping blood; but Bounce did not follow. His head was throbbing; he was nauseated by the reek of goat and his fury was spent. He tried to escape the clinging smell by bounding at high speed towards the heather line, but he could not shake it off. Every time he stopped it wafted into his nostrils in hot waves—sickly-sweet, cloying, with an elusive under-taint like the earth-scent of fox. When he reached the first birch thicket on the moor he thrashed the branches and rubbed flanks against burnished stems. He rolled and kicked till he bruised out tang from the heather. During the night he remained in the thicket, browsing on birch twigs and rolling on his back. But when the morning came, all silver frost and misted sunfire, the goat-smell was still with him.

During two snell days and starlit nights he mooched alone in the heather, and the worst of the goat-smell left him. In the cloudy daybreak of the third morning, when the first grey geese were flying south, he turned his nose for Glencryan. He stopped only twice on the way—once to

nibble blackberries nipped by frost; once to roll in a
frenzy in a bed of yellow tansy. Rain was falling when he
reached the wood, and when he found Sona and the
fawns the aromatic smell of tansy was rising from him in
waves. Sona, sniffing him over in greeting, parted her lips
in a grimace to show her disapproval of the tansy-taint he
had brought with him. The taint was still there when the
herd went out to feed at dusk.

During the frore days of the leaf-fall the deer paunched
heavily on doghips, lipping shrewdly round crimson tufts
of robin's pin-cushion which that year were thick on the
briars. They sought blackberries in the hedgerows, till
the spiked tendrils were shorn of their shrivelled leaves
and the last berries shrunken in the frost. They took haw
and acorn, and the boor tree's purple berries; then for two
days munched tough-skinned chestnuts which they found
among the layered fronds and prickly husks on the mould.
But the chestnut harvest was short, for Bodach, the
Glencryan badger, ate many. The rabbits nibbled them
too, and one morning the deer saw a big buck driving a
squirrel away from the harvest.

The deer fed well, even when the night frosts were keen;
they grew fat. Their winter coats came in dense and
grey, their throat flashes plain, their flags the colour of
faded rose leaves. Bounce cast his antlers in Glencryan
when the last lyart leaves were being stripped from the
oaks by the wind, and was brusque with the fawns till the
sores skinned over. Leaves drifted over the antlers, and
they were lost.

Fieldfares shredded the blistering doghips when the
horned moon was high at mid-morning; gangrel waxwings, airting south, gulped them whole. Golden plover,
that had known the roaring of the red stags in the high
corries, pitched whistling in the tawny moorland pastures

where black-face hoggs were on for the wintering. On the heather, only the grouse remained. Strange woodcock flitted, owl-like, in Glencryan. From the lochs, at darkening, came the wild cangling of geese and the whiplash whistle of wigeon. The wind settled into a steady blast from the east, and the mornings were suddenly snell and raw.

Bounce led the herd to the Stane Farm potato field where rooks were seeking chats among the frosted shaws. The deer bit potatoes on only one morning, and did not return to the field. They visited the turnips, which were shawed and laid out on the drills for fat cross-Leicester sheep. Rabbits and hares were there in the dark, feeding with the sheep—the hares stripping down the turnip skins before eating the heart, the rabbits chewing as they gnawed. The deer bit off scliffs, but ate little; they had no urgent need of potatoes or turnips, and were not eager.

December came dark and blustering, with daily rain; the deer fed wet and slept wet, losing condition. Bounce had antler buds in velvet before the first foxes were barking. More geese slanted down, and the stars at night had an icy brilliance. The east wind gusted and raged in a feeding storm. And one morning the sun rose, red and ragged, on a world in cranreuch, with the mole runs lined with iron and ice thick enough to support a roe. Ice cased the resting buds of beech and oak; the ivy leaves, unglazed by frost, were edged with rime. The deer coughed and their breath was vapour.

The snow came in goose-feather flakes that lay as they settled; they blotted out the sun. In the night the wood was a swirling chaos. The deer stayed in harbour, shaking off their mantle of snow. And at dawn, when it lay hock-deep, Bounce led the herd, high-stepping through the downswirl, to the familiar gloom of Dryflatts, knowing they would find dry harbours under the ample skirts of the spruces.

19

THE WINTER WAS HARD AND LONG, AND THE SNOW lay deep in the woods. For weeks the burns ran silent under glass-ice feathered with rime. Icicles, like otter tails, hung from the rock ledges where woodrush drooped; they were rowed like sharks' teeth under branches where water had dripped in a thaw. By day the wind skirled new threat of snow, and at night the frost powder drifted under the glittering stars.

Bounce trod his runways deep in Dryflatts and Glencryan; slotted by many hooves they radiated to birch thicket and blaeberry clump and windfall, and the deer moved from browse to browse without floundering in the drifts. Night and morning they pawed circular scrapes in the pastures, to bare the scanty grass. Rabbits followed them and grazed the green into the ground. Sheep skinned the bark from the branches of windfalls, and the grouse followed them where they trod out the snow from the heather. Goldcrest and wren and fieldfare died in the snow, and lay with legs stretched and slim talons clenched till devoured by fox or badger. One Eye moved to Stane Farm, where the rats were legion; but on Dryflatts Tufter was shrivelled with famine, hungering alone because his mate of many seasons was dead.

Foxes, bold with famine and hunting in couple, troubled the deer, mooching after the herds seeking weaklings. And weaklings were many among the old year's fawns. Sona's little buck fawn wandered away on his own before the first full moon of the year, and died under a crushing weight of frozen snow that had gathered on his shoulders after he had been drenched with sleet. The doe fawn remained with her mother, but she was lean and rough of coat and tired quickly in the drifts. The foxes marked her, and bided their time.

Bounce always faced the wind when it brought fox-smell to his nose, and kept his eyes on the reynards when they padded past, slit-eyed, breathing vapour.

One night he was lying in the lee of the spruces, with doe and fawn, sheltered by ample, snow-draped fronds from the dying blasts of a storm. Stray snowflakes, swirling under the spruce canopy, mottled the flanks of the deer for a brief moment, then dissolved into webs of water on a few coarse outer hairs. All three were wideawake, resting with their backs to the wind. Their paunches were slack. They had not seen a single living thing since lying down, although Bounce, turning his head when the air came suddenly pungent, knew that a band of marauding stoats had passed close behind him.

Musk smell on the wind brought him uneasily to his knees, with hindlegs braced to thrust. The doe, hearing the movement, looked round. As she turned her head away again Bounce leaped to his feet and whipped round into the wind, with nostrils aquiver and ears out-topping his growing horns. He stamped with a forefoot, and barked twice, bringing doe and fawn on foot beside him. All three stood tense, with ears forward and nostrils wide. Forty yards away they placed a fox—a white-spotted, black smudge against the snow—coming diagonally in their direction. The fox was The Limper.

He was coming along the face of a rise, with brush held clear of the snow, picking his way like a cat through a puddle, shaking a paw at every step. With uncanny instinct he was avoiding the deep pockets on the unfamiliar ground; The Limper was a moor fox born and bred

who rarely ranged north of Glencryan. He was down
from the bleak, hungry moor, seeking hens at low farms,
having raided Stane till every likely place was trapped
and every bird was under lock and key. His vixen was off
on another ploy, and he was hunting alone.

Up to the moment that Bounce barked The Limper
had not the remotest idea that he was so close to deer,
for he was on the wrong side of them to get their wind.
The buck's attitude did not daunt him at once. Big and
powerful though he was, his courage was tempered with
wisdom. He knew he was no match for a mature buck
under any kind of circumstances; but he also knew the
deer were more likely to yield ground than fight. So he
ettled to see if he could stampede them, to discover how
the fawn fared in the drifts. If it bogged down his mate
could be quickly summoned.

But The Limper had misjudged the haughty buck
standing taut before him. In the half-minute that he sat
on his hunkers, pondering and getting his brush clogged
with frozen snow, Bounce stamped like a ewe till his
blood ran hot with anger. When The Limper moved he
was set for war.

The fox rose slowly, with a great show of indifference.
He took four paces forward, stopped, bit at imaginary
fleas on his shoulder, all the time keeping his eye on the
deer. Then he moved nearer—slowly, stiff-legged, with
back arched and brush drawn into his hocks, displaying his
teeth in a noiseless snarl. Bounce stood firm. When the
fox was within twenty feet of him he reared up suddenly,
standing high and steady as he did when berry-gathering,
and pawed the air with his forehooves. That was his
warning—a warning of deadly import, conveyed by a
posture of elegance and grace.

The sign was not lost on The Limper. He turned away
with elaborate casualness, meaning to withdraw with

unhurried dignity; but he was not allowed such a salve to his pride. Bounce moved forward swiftly, reared again, and struck out with his forefeet. The blow would have cracked the fox's ribs if it had made contact. It didn't. As Bounce came down, chiselling deep slots in the snow, The Limper was yards away—pitching on his face, floundering belly deep, crackling the withered bracken tips showing above the drifts. On the wind-swept crest he trod on a stick lying coggley across a stone. It upended and hit him smartly in the face, which was the final ignominy, for he back-tracked and fled thinking it was a trap.

Such was the first encounter; but Bounce knew it would not be the last so long as famine gripped the bellies of the hunters. There were other unaccustomed perils. A great gathering of stoats was harrying the moor—hunting hares and rabbits; slaying grouse in their snow burrows; entering henhouses through rat-holes in rotten floor boards; driving even the foxes before them. One sunset they roused a polecat-ferret from a rabbit burrow and coursed it across the snow. The roe crossed their path when they were fanning in for the kill and buck and doe had to kick and stamp and tread to fight clear while the polecat was pinned down and slain under a smother of ermines.

More snow fell and froze and the east wind's icy talons took daily toll. Emaciated rabbits fell easy prey to foxes rib-taut with hunger. After five days of fasting the Glencryan badgers ranged far for braxies; they clawed through the frost crust of the Stane Farm midden seeking hen wings and feet, carrot tops. fish heads and peelings of potatoes. Unable to scrape down to grass the deer browsed hardwood and briar, rhododendron, larch and juniper. Many roe died; Bounce and Sona grew lean, and the doe fawn sickened.

During a blizzard of Polar fury the Dryflatts spruces fell in swathes and the deer left the wood. Fine snow billowed up as the spruces crashed and was tossed away by the wind: far out, the fields were strewn with twigs and spruce fronds and the sticks of old nests. Bounce struck out, floundering across belly-deep snow, with doe and fawn rearing and plunging in his tracks. The wind furrowed their flags and heaped their rumps with snow.

Two hours before dawn they were resting under elms beside a farm, drooping and winded, blowing vapour in clouds, their legs covered with burrs of frozen snow. The farm was dark and muffled; the windows drifted up. The deer high-stepped into the dark stackyard where rows of leets, snug and dry under their thatch of snow, were a beild against the storm.

The wind died in flurries of snow; the sky cleared. Hares were in the kitchen garden, scraping for kale custocks. In the dark, cushats swung down to an opened leet to pull straws with their beaks; below them, burrowed in straw at the base, a fox was lying, waiting for one to flap down after dropped ickers. The deer, following turnip smell, sheered away from the fox, and found a great heap of purple swedes covered with straw. A white owl, spying for rats from a leet-top, watched them as they scraped and swivelled his head when he heard the crunch of teeth.

The roe bit eagerly at cold, frosted turnips. Suddenly, the cushats exploded from the leet-top with a wild clatter of wings. The deer, holding their bite, looked round. The fox was in the open, with a flapping pigeon pinned down in the snow. In a moment it was dead, its neck a raggle of blood, and he was up and away across the packed snow of the closs with the prey in his jaws. The owl wafted from his perch, shrieking. Cocks crowed. The dogs in the stable set up a frenzied barking. The deer, chewing on their bite, back-tracked from the turnip heap and scrambled reluctantly away on their incoming line.

Bounce did not return to the shambles of Dryflatts. He led doe and fawn floundering across white fields and drifted hollows till they reached a half-acre planting of young larch on a south-lying slope. The guard-netting was drifted over, and rabbits were inside, barking the tallest trees and eating out leaders where the snow was deep. Deep, oval fox slots, triangular slots of pheasants, and the neat presses of voles were everywhere in the planting. The roe ploughed over the netting, reached out hungry muzzles, and filled their paunches with larch twigs for the first time in their lives. Then they scraped beds in the deep snow and lay down in the sparse cover for the day.

They left in the late afternoon, when the sun was flashing rays of lambent gold across the yowdendrift and a mist of amethyst, tenuous as breath vapour, skeined the Dryflatts larches. Their hooves slotted deep, and their clett-tips gashed the snow. Shadows shaped the tracks of many feet in the field—partridge, crow, pheasant, fox, badger, rabbit and the big two-in-line-ahead and two-side-by-side slots of a hare. On the north side of Dryflatts a big fox was crouched like a carving under a thick hawthorn growing on the lip of the burn. The deer did not change direction; they were walking easily on packed snow and Bounce minced up to within twenty paces before halting to ponder.

The fox lifted lips to show teeth and Bounce saw movement in the thorn. Down the scabbed and green-velveted trunk a bright-eyed woodmouse was climbing, her fairy feet as confident as a squirrel's on the rough bark. In her teeth she held a lustreless haw which she had just taken from her store in a snow-filled thrush's nest higher up in the tree. As she scurried from the thorn the fox flicked a forepaw and smashed her into the snow. She squeaked as the blow killed her, and her incisor teeth skinned the haw when they bit tight in death. The fox snatched up the body, shook it clear of snow, and bolted it whole with a single click of teeth.

The roe entered the wood on the heels of the fox and were slowed down in the wreckage of windfalls; the storm had blasted a wide avenue of daylight through the spruce gloom. Line after line of spruces lay flat, with their crowns buried in drifts; many leaned against other trees still swaying from root-holds; the trunks of some had broken. In the clearing, the snow was layered green with fronds and the air had a resinous tang. Bounce, not liking the tightly wedged shambles, led the herd out to face the long flounder to Glencryan.

Beneath the far-spreading branches of a massive beech they scraped their lies, pawing right down to the icy mould, which they scored and gouged with their hooves. The fawn tired quickly; she had hollows behind her ribs. One Eye, the tawny owl, flapped into the beech and jumped down from branch to branch to watch, with his neck stretched and hooked beak buried in his frill. The deer hip-rolled in the hollows they had made and lay down to chew cud. They used the same lairs for many days, and the snow under the beech became brown-stained and slotted and littered with droppings.

Into the wood one night, when the moon was full and Orion glittering, came a great dark bird with almost the bulk of an eagle, flying in tired moth flight about twenty feet above its own wavering ground shadow. Three roe stood rigid in birch cover as the dread shape passed over; One Eye, on his roost, inflated his throat but no sound came from him. The apparition swept silently into a shaggy-headed pine, where it shuffled on a branch and raised feather tufts like horns on its head. The moonlight revealed it as an owl—an owl with eyes bright and flaming as a leopard's—a Grand Duc or eagle owl; the most savagely powerful of the clan, who feared nothing that walked or crawled or flew. He had come by estuary of Forth, blown across the North Sea from some scarred, primeval forest where the elk still roams; from some Baltic fastness, or Tannenberg, or forests that were once part of the empire of the Tsar.

The Grand Duc edged along his pine roost out of the glare of the moon; he ruffled breast feathers over talons, hunched his shoulders, and slept. One Eye flapped silently away. Bounce loped quietly to the northside fence, with doe and fawn running nose to flag in his slots. They browsed saugh twigs along the burn, then moved to the Stane Farm lane for briar and aspen and trailing tendrils of bramble, feeding far into the night. When they returned to the wood the moon was near setting; dark and moveless the beech shadows lay aslant the snow. The night was all frost and star-glitter—and silence. The deer filed, vapouring, to harbour.

Kveck-kveck!

The outlandish cry shocked the silence, alarming and alerting the deer. A monstrous shadow wavered over the moon-washed snow. The Grand Duc was a-wing, flapping in level flight under the beech canopy, soundless as his own shadow—an alien with tremendous talons, edged like knives, and a rending beak that could rip the throat from a goose.

Kveck-kveck!

He was wheeling as he called. He winnowed low over the snow; then, suddenly, he had swept up, and turned steeply, to swoop at the fawn with ear tufts flat and talons clutching. Bounce reared as the fawn jumped, and the owl swerved away. *Kveck-kveck!* The sickle beak opened and closed twice and the cry came on puffs of misted breath. The Grand Duc, at tree height, wheeled to strike again. Bounce, though he knew fear, stood resolute; but doe and fawn broke away. The giant shape launched after them. The fawn, with a wild cry of terror, crashed into the dense, dark crown of a fallen spruce and cowered trembling astride the stem at its heart. *Kveck-kveck!* With his mighty wings buffeting the spruce fronds the Grand Duc scrambled for a foothold. Hearing the beat of wings against spruce branch and foliage the cushats exploded from oak and pine roost. The fawn wailed. Then a dark shape reared and struck at the owl and the great bird lifted away with a startled yelp. Bounce had leaped to the attack.

He slotted the snow with his stamping while the Grand Duc circled above the pines on wings as noiseless as sleep. Up there, he was beyond seeing; and when he dropped from the dark tops, attacking from behind, he caught the buck off guard. His talons scored Bounce's neck, then he was up and away, an immense drifting shadow, flaming-eyed, turning steeply for another assault. Bounce, now close to breaking, back-tracked and pressed his flag hard into the spruce fronds, protecting his back while he kept his eyes on the owl.

The Grand Duc swooped again, but it was an attempt to stampede rather than a full-blooded attack, and he sheered away when the buck stood firm. Twice more he planed in, with wings up-held and padded legs stretched, but each time he threw up without striking, and banked widely away. He glided low over the spruce, brushing the needles with his wings; he swept up and turned and breasted the green fronds again; but his resolution was melting. At each turn, he was coming over higher. And at last he swung up, dipped flat from the turn, and glided away in low, rocking flight through the beeches, yelping as he flew.

Sona trotted up when his yelping died away, and thrust her muzzle into the spruce cover to reassure her fawn. Bounce, relaxing, rubbed an antler against his knee. The little doe came out of her cover, weak and shaken, sniffed her mother's muzzle, and followed stumbling to harbour.

The moon had set when their ears heard the tread of hasty feet on frozen snow. A big hare was racing in the wood, with head up and ears flat, skimming fast over the drifts on snow-shoe feet. From the darkness above him a great shadow fell and struck. Vast, downy wings spread, buffeting, above the fleeing hare, and talons reached down. The hare's despairing skelloch brought the roe to their feet, stamping disapproval. Then the Grand Duc was down in the snow, balancing with his wings, while his claws tore the life from his prey. And presently the hare's sobbing was stilled, and the owl folded his wings. He reached down with his sickle beak and tore off great gobs of flesh, which he swallowed with much neck stretching and blinking of heavy lids over flaming, orange eyes. And when his hunger was sated he flapped to a tall pine, leaving the mangled remains lying in the snow.

At first light two blackbirds and a blue tit were flying to and fro, pecking freezing flesh from the disembowelled hare. The deer, following their flight with their eyes, saw Bodach, the old boar badger, prowling in the wood. Bodach, sniffing in an arc, found the blood scent on the wind and raced to the carrion. He straddled it at once, grunting warning of possession. The Grand Duc, unlidding savage eyes, watched without moving to interfere; he inflated his throat but did not cry out. Unlike the hunting beasts he had little sense of ownership. Bodach, snatching up the prey, carried it to a thicket, where he devoured it down to the last wisp of fur. The Grand Duc rolled down his lids and slept.

Many days before the east wind launched its final offensive of snow the sheep were on the lower ground feeding on hay; and when the foxes and crows had devoured the last exposed braxies the hunger talons raked their bellies. The stoat pack, running riot, left a trail of slaughtered hens, and blood splashes, ringed with grouse feathers, on the snow. The deer trod the old sheep walks in Glencryan, tramping down the snow, and after the storm their runways were shoulder deep in the drifts. Thus they travelled freely to points nearest their browse before floundering out to feed, returning to their runways when they wanted to shift ground.

They were in a birch thicket, browsing hock-deep in snow, their shadows projected long in the revealing light of a lop-sided moon, when they heard the dread cry in the wood. *Kveck-kveck!* All three high-stepped to the runway, their bellies balled with snow, and faced the sound with ears up and slim legs rigid. No dark wings were flapping in the moonlight; but Bounce, searching also with ears and nose, heard the whisper of pads on frozen snow and found fox-smell on the wind.

There were four foxes prowling—two upwind giving their scent to distract the deer, and two downwind belly-crawling close in a crafty stalk. The doe, glancing nervously over her shoulder, spied the pair she couldn't smell and wheeled smartly to face them, stamping a fore-hoof. Bounce looked round, and saw, then turned back to keep track of the upwind pair. They were working in one on each side of the runway, with heads low, eyes slitted, and brushes held clear of the snow. Bounce laid back his ears, and the spring came into his knee. Then . . .

Kveck-kveck!

Three roe and four foxes pricked ears to hearken. Wide wings blotted out the moon for the space of a heart-beat, then the Grand Duc was swooping. Down he came with a terrible cry—wide-eyed, immense and menacing, with legs outstretched and talons spread. He sailed low over the snow, banked and struck—at one of the stalking foxes! Bounce whipped round in his slots to check downwind,

237

knocking against the fawn, who was wedged between him and the doe. Behind him two foxes paused to ponder.

The Grand Duc flapped up with a foot full of fur. The assaulted fox leaped up, chopping and yelping, and got his mask laid open by a lightning stroke from a second set of talons. Then the second fox jumped, snapping, and the Grand Duc felt the pinch of teeth and lost down from a leg. Buffeting clear, he wavered low above the runway, with two foxes in pursuit, and struck savagely at the fawn. But the doe reared, and the fawn crouched, and he swooshed up and clear without touching a hide.

The foxes closed in behind the owl, chopping to stampede the doe; the upwind beasts bellied down and moved forward to test the mettle of the buck. Bounce threatened with his head, then reared, and dog fox and vixen cringed back from his flashing hooves. The Grand Duc, swinging high to check positions before renewing his assault, saw the buck striking out at two foxes with his forehooves while the other pair backed away before the doe. Uttering his wild, ringing war-whoop he tilted forward and dived.

Bounce made contact with a hoof as the Grand Duc swooped, and the dog fox lurched away drunkenly with his face laid open and an ivory tusk loose in his jaw. The second fox of the pair lost heart when she had to face the fiery buck alone, and slunk away after her wounded mate. Bounce, savage in victory, struck out at her rump, then turned to help his doe as the Grand Duc flashed past his shoulder. Enraged at the sight of the owl he bounded up to Sona and shouldered her aside to face foxes and Grand Duc himself. But at that point he received an unexpected ally.

The Grand Duc, instead of attacking the fawn, wafted over her head and flew straight at the face of the nearest fox—the mate of the beast whose mask he had already slashed. But she was wise, and swift, and her actions followed her thinking like one heart-beat on another, so she saved her eyes by turning away and pressing her face against the side of the runway. The Grand Duc, hanging poised for a moment above her, was almost trodden into the snow by the assaulting buck.

He escaped the flailing hooves by a miracle, and flapped into the air with a strident scream. Both foxes leaped from the runway and fled across the snow, their zest for deer completely forgotten. Bounce plunged after them for perhaps fifty yards, bogging in the drifts, skidding where the snow was glazed, then returned winded to the herd. By then, the Grand Duc was in a tree, blinking his eyes, resting before attacking again.

But the more he looked at the roe the less he liked the situation, for buck and doe were close together, with the fawn between them. He could have gone in; and he could have killed. But he knew the price would be high, things being as they were. The buck was in fighting mood, the doe set for war. So he snapped his beak, tissed like a cat, sounded his battle cry twice, then launched away to seek less dangerous prey.

When the thaw came the fawn was thin, her rump drawn down and her hindlegs stiff. The snow shrank slowly, rain-washed by day and glassed by frost in the night. Long after the rooks were nesting it lay in long ridges on the north side of hedgerows and in deep pockets on slopes lying from the sun. At Hoolet Nest, yellow coltsfoot opened among stones below the wall while migrant wheatears *chakked* and flirted tails on drifts deeper than the sagging garden fence.

On the low ground the snow-fed waters spread; ditches and burns ran full and gulls sailed and preened on flooded stubbles. Dripping icicles, loosened like decayed tusks in the thaw, fell with minute clatter and were gathered by the rushing water. Curlews bubbled on the moor, and above the wet, dark ploughland peewits tumbled and threw about the windy sky.

On a misted morning of low clouds and no wind the deer were lying on the south side of Braeburn, where the old bracken was warm. From Dryflatts came the whine of saws and the crash of branches; down there men were clearing the windfalls. In the bare Braeburn larches cushats were crooing. The deer, couched upright, licked knee and shoulder, and rubbed muzzles in the bracken.

For long minutes the deer watched three carrion crows yarring and posturing in a tall roadside thorn. Then there was uproar in the long pasture between Braeburn and Glencryan. Down the slope, flying low, came a vast flock of rooks—a ragged circus on ragged wings—cawing and wheeling and diving in obvious anger. A fox appeared, running down a rigg ahead of his tormentors. Bounce heard the roar of a lorry on the road as the fox reached the bottom of the field. Gulls, peewits, cushats, crows and golden plover rose in a wild scatter of wings and fled in a bewildering criss-cross of movement. The fox raced for the road, shied away when the lorry stopped at a gate, and turned right about when Pate Tamson jumped down from the cabin with Sam the lurcher. Pate, with ferret in bag and pocket stuffed with purse nets, had travelled with the swill lorry from Skeoch Farm.

The lurcher shot away when Pate shouted *Fetch*, and the fox streaked along the woodside with Sam thirty yards behind. Sam lost ground when a bold rook, swooping at the fox, almost hit him on the face. Bounce lost track of the chase when the fox ran close to the wood, but he sensed they were coming his way. In a few moments a very frightened vixen shot over the rotted netting on the old drystane dyke and flashed past him into the wood.

Alarmed because she had brought the hunt so close the deer jumped to their feet, and bounded into a thicket, to let the dog have a clear run with nothing to distract him.

But their move to safety was a move into danger, for the lurcher, overshooting the vixen's turning-off point by twenty yards, leaped over the dyke without casting back, knowing he would cross her line in the wood. Instead, he ran full tilt into the deer.

Sam forgot the fox, because he was a deer killer by instinct and free-willed when beyond instructions. In his eagerness to rush to the worry he fell on his muzzle at the jump-down. Bounce spurned larch needles and leaped away, with doe and fawn crashing behind. Fear gave added strength to his legs. Waywise among the crowded larches he went through in fantastic bounds at a speed which Sam could not hope to equal in the heavy cover. And the vixen, after circling and running foil, watched the hunt go by.

Bounce crackled through brittle brushwood. He slid down a slope, ploughing wet larch needles with his cletts, and crashed through screening alders into the burn. Doe and fawn were still running in his slots. He ran the burn for twenty yards, clambered out on the far side, ran the bank for twenty more, then returned to the water. Here the burn was shallow, fast-flowing over a pebbly bottom, and he lapped as he trotted till he reached a bend, where it was belly-deep and overhung with willows. A heron, standing rigid with unwinking eyes and down-pointing javelin beak, watching for beardies among the stones, rose with heavy flap of wings when the deer splashed from the water. Bounce bounded clear of the last cover and turned left for Glencryan.

The lurcher lost the line at the burn, and his tail went down. Forgetting the deer as he had forgotten the fox, he trotted from the wood, breathing lightly with tongue quivering over his wolfish teeth. And in the open he saw the deer, coming right across his front on their way to Glencryan. Like a greyhound from the trap he shot out to head them.

The fawn was in distress, and cried when the lurcher ran at her. Staring-eyed, with tongue showing, she broke away from him, running a circle like a doe circling a man who threatens her fawn. Bounce trotted on an outer circle, stiff-necked, with the spring in his knee, but did not attack. Twice, when the fawn cried out, he stopped to stamp—and bark—with ears flattened. Up on the headrigg the doe stood, with ears up, watching. . . .

Sam ran the fawn in a tight ring, mute, wearing her down, and when she stumbled, crying like a child, he leaped upon her, pawed her down, and worried her where she fell. And while the warm blood thrilled his tongue Bounce paraded stiffly on a widening circuit, threatening without interfering. Then, when the moocher appeared, running across the field, he bounded away to join the doe on the headrigg at Glencryan.

— 20 —

FIVE DAYS AFTER THE SWALLOWS WERE TWITTERING at Stane Farm, Bounce cleaned velvet in Braeburn, rubbing against young larch stems on which the bark had not hardened. He cleaned a full six-point head, with shafts closely pearled and long white tines like polished ivory dirks. By the time the swallows were nesting, carrying dunged mud from lane puddle and gateway, the horns had matured to the colour of pine bark and only the tine tips were white.

After the long snow, the young grass came quickly with primrose and ripening catkin in the warm April days and the deer, grazing at darkening with the sheep, regained condition. They browsed sappy twigs of thorn and sallow, and when they went to harbour in the morning their paunches were full. But both looked unkempt, for their coats were patchy in the moult—a mixture of foxy red and tousy winter grey.

Bounce was mouthing an old puff-ball fungus, weathered to the colour of peat and the toughness of cork, when he heard the barking of terriers in the Stane Farm lane. At first, he heard without heeding. He played with the puff-ball, rolling it in his mouth, tossing it in the air, and making mock thrusts at it with his antlers when it fell. Above him, One Eye was watching, blinking his eye and crooning low in his throat. The owl was roosting beside the old nest of a cushat, in which he had dropped a fat vole and a shrew that morning; before sunset he would carry them to his mate on the nest, when her first owlet would have hatched.

Sona came to Bounce when the terriers barked in the wood. She was taut and nervous, remembering the fox hunts during the last days of snow, when dogs and beaters and men with guns had stormed every thicket in Glencryan. Bounce, also remembering, dropped his woody puff-ball and ran with her to the moor edge. There, among the old bracken tangles, they stopped, unmoving, matching their cover, to hark back with ears, nose and eyes to the barking in the wood.

But they heard neither voices nor the beating of sticks, for only Pate Tamson and the shepherd were in the wood, seeking denned vixens with terriers. One terrier was rioting after rabbits and the recall whistles had no meaning for the deer. Presently they saw the bounding shapes of roe far out on the heather; the switch-horn, with doe and follower, were breaking out after lying close till men and dogs had passed. Then Bounce saw a yearling buck stumbling from the wood, running a losing race against the rioting terrier.

Fluked and wasting, the young buck had been roused on foot by the near barking of the dog. Three crows, who had been watching him in his lair, circled out with the chase to keep him in view. The buck lurched in the deep heather, and fell. He rose again, staggering sideways, before the terrier could come up, and ran in a curve till he reached a dub of water among roe-high seedling birches. Spent and trembling, with ribbed flanks heaving, he stood knee-deep in dark peaty water, with slim neck drooping, tongue showing, and cream flag frilled down like a flower after rain. He had small antler buds still in velvet.

The terrier was small and wiry, with otter face and dark muzzle, and a white star on her breast. She leaped at the buck with the savagery of a wolf. The buck, back-stepping, hunkered in the water and was seized by the throat. For a brief moment he found strength to fight up his head, with the dog, kicking and gurrying, fastened to his throat; then he was down on his side, kicking feebly, and the water rushed in his lungs. His white gorget was stained with his blood. And presently he was dead, worried and drowned by a boot-high terrier he could have maimed with a hoof stroke in his days of strength.

Growling and coughing water, the terrier worried on long after he was dead. She tugged at his throat—swimming, treading water, bobbing under and coming up retching, without once loosing her hold—and soon she had the body at the edge of the dub, with the bloody muzzle aground. Only then did she lose interest, and after shaking her coat clear of water she raced back to the men, with tail tucked down knowing she would be rated. When she had gone the crows flapped down to the dub, and with their ebony beaks pecked out the buck's eyes and stabbed knowingly at his tongue.

Bounce and Sona lay up in the warm bracken during the soft rain of the day and their coats, darkening, itched. They saw two men and three terriers leaving the wood, the moocher with a big fox brush and five smaller brushes of cubs hanging on a string from the belt round his waist. All day they heard the faint, rasping whine of saws in Dryflatts, and sometimes the distant crash of timber when a swaying tree was felled.

At nightfall, they grazed slowly back to Glencryan. A woodcock was roding round One Eye's roosting tree, unalarmed by the hooting of the owl in the wood. The deer kneed down to cud as One Eye flew to his mate with a rat held by the neck in his beak, and in a moment the owls were mewing on the nest, greeting each other with spread tails and quivering wings. When the moon's crescent was pale in the dawn-light Bounce rose and loped with Sona through the shadowy beechwood to the

heather, where they found Bodach and his mate gorging
on the carcase of the dead buck, which they had dragged
clear of the water. Bounce stamped when the blood smell
came distastefully to his nostrils, but felt no enmity
towards the grunting brocks.

From that day no foxing terriers came to the wood,
and the deer were not disturbed. They grew fat. Badgers,
foxes, crows, magpies and tits fed on the flesh of the buck
till ribs, neck and rump were bare and tufts of brittle
hair lay scattered among the birches. A black crow forced
his way behind the ribs to eat pulped carrion, but a fox
moved the carcase and he could not force his way out
again. So he ate till there was nothing left to eat, and died
of hunger and thirst in the chest of a roe.

The oak leaves were unfolding, ruddy in the sun, before
the roe lost the last of their matted winter grey. Their
flags came in snow-white, flushed with rose at the frill.
Bounce, in new coat of prime fox-red, was grizzled of face,
strong of antler, with one white flash persisting on his
throat—a master buck in the full flush of his power.

Summer came with a rush of green. Wild liquorice and
hogweed, angelica and parsley, thrust up along fence and
hedgerow and the wood was clothed. Bees drowsed in the
horse chestnut candles. Cuckoos called all day, and three
tawny owlets flew in Glencryan. In the dark, their wild
cries rang through the wood. When twin badger cubs
were making furtive forays from their den, and pine
pollen, blown by the wind, ringed with gold-dust the
rippled wood pools, Sona left in the night to seek her
secret place of travail.

Within sight and hearing of Stane Farm she found a
two-acre planting of seedling Norway spruces, netted
round against rabbits; the young trees were overgrown
with nettles, bleached grass and foxgloves, and the cover
was thick. During the night, and half of the next daylight,

Sona lay close among the spruces, and in the early afternoon, when cushats were crooning from leafy branches in
the heat of the sun, she gave birth to a single spotted fawn,
which kicked as she licked it dry. She nursed him, lying
down, till the coming of dusk; then, touching him gently
with her muzzle, she rose, and left him, and leaped over
the netting to feed.

But Sona had chosen unwisely, for when the morning
came three men arrived with hand scythes to cut the
growth from the spruce seedlings, and all day she was
kept away from her fawn. The men, seeing her running
in the field, and standing for long periods, with ears up,
watching them, wondered at her behaviour without
immediately guessing the cause. Sona's anxiety gnawed
at her during the long working day and when the men
left at last, still talking of her behaviour, she returned
swiftly to her fawn.

He was hungry and shivering and again she had to
nurse him lying down. Many times in the night she stood
for him while he groped with his baby lips under her flank,
knock-kneed and splay-legged as he dunted at her udder.
In the first pallor of daybreak he followed her to the netting. She called to him urgently, *whee-yoo! Eep-eep* he
answered her, unable to follow. She leaped back into the
planting, leaped out again, calling him. Still he *peeped* to
her, touching her muzzle with his tongue through the
mesh. Spring-footed, Sona ran up and down the outside
of the netting; the fawn, stumbling along the inside,
followed her till he was exhausted. When the men came
back on the second morning he was still imprisoned in the
planting.

That morning one of the labourers came armed with
a shotgun which he kept close at hand as he scythed down
the nettles. The fawn, lying near the far-side netting, with
muzzle resting on up-gathered hindlegs, heard without

pricking his ears to hearken. He lay still, but sometimes a tremor passed over his flanks when he breathed deeply.

Sona stayed out of sight till mid-morning, when anxiety for her fawn brought her back to the planting. The men watched her as she paraded up and down, some distance from the netting. Once she jumped inside, but her courage melted, and she jumped out again without going to her fawn. Nor did she call him on foot. From time to time the labourer tried to stalk her in his fashion, crawling with the gun held forward in his hands; but she marked him long before he was within range and bounded nervously away.

At midday the men sat down to eat and drink tea from flasks, and afterwards they lay flat in a hollow among the spruces, watching the doe. Birds flittered to the netting, then into the planting—coal-head, tam tit and moss cheeper—all carrying food for chicks in the tussocks. A cock partridge, with chestnut horseshow on breast, pecked among the dung pats in the field, where young peewits were running. Sona stood unmoving, with ears erect, staring towards the men, while a skylark flew down twice beside her with food and was met by half-fledged chicks running from their nest. She was anxious, and pained by gathering milk; she forgot. She nibbled self heal and clover, touched muzzle to shoulder, and walked mincingly towards the netting.

The shotgun roared while she was still too far out, but the pellets spattered at her feet and some stung her hooves and legs. In one wild bound she was out of range. Slewing round she halted, faced the planting, stamped with a forefoot, and barked. And many things happened at once.

Cushats crashed from the trees across the road. A hen pheasant burst from the heart of the planting, scattering downy chicks which had been burrowing in the feathers of her thighs. A big doe hare, giving birth to leverets near the spot where the fawn was lying, leaped away over the spruce tops with ears laid back and blood on her fud. From the top of the field Fraser of Stane Farm came running. Sona stood still, watching the planting. The men rose into view. Fraser slowed to a walk, wondering why she was not hearing him. He came on quietly, till he was close enough to touch her. He touched her. There was a split second's time lag between the touch and the turn of her head. Then she saw, and was away in great bounds to the roadside fence, where she stopped to watch the new menace to her fawn.

Fraser was a man who could sned heads with his tongue. He was as hard as concrete, but had an understanding heart towards everything except foxes and crows. And he had known Sanshach.

"Whae fired the shote?" he glowered at the men. Then, without waiting for an answer; "Keep that bliddy gun on your ain side o' the fence! The next time you poke it oot you'll be talkin' tae the polis. Whit the hell are you daein onyway, shootin' at a deer?"

"It was the boss . . ." began the man with the gun. "Thur young trees. . . . The deer wid . . ."

"The bliddy deer's no meddlin' your trees!" shouted Fraser in his best inter-county voice. "If you'd ony gumption you'd ken . . ." an he stopped there, realising they didn't know what he had already guessed. "Tell your heid puddock fae me this is ma grun, an' I'm no havin' naebody—*naebody*—shootin' at deer, inside or oot!"

And Fraser stamped away.

The men worked till the sun was red and Sona circled the planting at intervals, in an agony of apprehension for her fawn. Larks were still singing when Bounce came round the farm from Glencryan and saw her on the head-rigg. He ran to her. She muzzled him, and butted his flank, and he raked her playfully with his antlers. And when the men left at last he followed her to the planting.

Whee-yoo! she called when she leaped inside. *Eep-eep!* The fawn answered in a weak voice, and, sprackling to his feet, stumbled to meet her. Bounce sniffed his head, his flank, his flag, then turned to snatch mouthfuls of grass which the men had cut the day before. The fawn reached under Sona's flank, greedy for milk, but as his lips found her nipple she stepped roughly away, squeaking, and dunting him with her head till he kneed down and flattened among the spruces. Then she bounded away with Bounce. Fraser of Stane Farm was crossing the field.

The farmer smiled as he climbed over the fence into the planting. *So you've gotten your mannie in tae*, he mused, casting round with his eyes before starting to walk slowly along the inside of the netting. From the far side of the planting he was watched by the deer. Bounce stamped sharply and barked at the man; Sona added her terrier *yap* to the gruff *boughing* of her mate. Fraser turned at the bottom netting, stepped six yards sideways, and came back on a straight line parallel to his own dew-tracks. The doe started to circle him, holding close to the netting; Bounce stamped angrily and barked at intervals. Fraser plodded on, quartering the planting. The hen pheasant burst from his feet, whirred up and flattened out, and flew rocking and *kooking* away. The farmer stepped carefully, in case he trampled cheepers. And then he found the fawn.

Sona circled faster than before. Bounce closed in to half distance and *boughed* angrily at the man. Fraser picked up the fawn with calloused, gentle hands. *Man, there's no muckle o' ye at that*, he reflected aloud, as was his habit. He walked quickly to the netting, climbed over with the fawn under his oxter, and put him down a little way out in the field. Dusk was gathering fast. Up in Glencryan One Eye was hooting. The lights were on at the farm. Fraser looked back, and saw the deer running up to the netting. He smiled, and shook his head.

"Come and get it!" he called to them, and left. And, from the headrigg, he watched Sona nursing her fawn before leading him away from the perilous neighbourhood of the planting.

Bounce and Sona harboured in Glencryan in the long summer days, and the fawn, having no brother or sister to share the doe's milk, grew quickly. At night, when the doe was feeding with Bounce, he nibbled hawthorn leaves and blaeberry, succulent stems of brooklime, sourock, speedwell and the leaves of the plantain. And many times he fought Bounce in the misty daybreak, butting at his flank while Bounce hooked round playfully with his antlers. When the corn was ripening he was a grushie little buck, waywise and fox-wise, slim of leg and sleek, who could lose the fleetest dogs in the wood.

But the easy cameraderie with Bounce had to come to an end; and one morning, when the fawn pranced up to the attack, he was warned off by hoof-stamps and an antlered head lowered in threat. Sensing the change in the temper of the old buck, the fawn did not bore in as was his wont; he ran at once to his mother and butted sticks and ferns instead. But his ears were hearkening to Bounce, and from time to time he looked round to watch him pawing under birch scrogs and thrashing branches with his horns.

From that day Bounce was haughty towards the fawn. He allowed the little buck to sniff him, and sniffed in return; but at the first sign of mock-attack his neck stiffened and his head went down in unmistakable warning. The fire was kindling in him, and he was restless by day—parading stiff-necked in the beechwood; scraping with his forehooves in the mould; prodding viciously at every low forked branch that looked like horns. At night, he blazed down in fury on any callow fox sapling who crossed his path; he threatened hares when they intruded near his hoof-scrapes; and once he drove away an immense cock capercaillie, all beard and beetle green, with bright crimson wattle. Sona eluded him each time he flanked her to put his chin on her withers, and enticed him to chase her to the lekking ground of the blackcock, where their ring of the previous autumn was grown over with rank grass and blue-bells.

Three roe barking at once in Glencryan, in the mist and drizzle of a windless daybreak, brought him running from the hayfield where he had been dirking rucks with his antlers. Sona, grazing clover leaves in the foggage by the woodside fence, looked up as he bounded past, and squeaked to her fawn; but she did not follow him when he leaped the fence. In the birch thickets Bounce stopped to thrash branches, and stamp in the soggy ground till he was sleeked to the knees with peaty glaur. For a minute afterwards he stood motionless, with head high and ears forward; then, wary and fox-footed, he minced from the thicket.

They were on the beechwood edge, gouging the mould with their hooves—the switch-horn and two sapling bucks—grunting and stabbing in a two-to-one fight, which is rare among roe. The young bucks were two-year-olds, wearing pronged antlers; the horns of the switch were draidlets—pale, smooth dags totally unlike his great rapier weapons of former years. One of the pronghorns was raking the switch's flank while the other engaged his head. The old buck's ribs were bleeding; he had been stabbed many times. As Bounce watched he was lifted almost bodily against the furrowed trunk of an up-branching beech, and in an instant both attackers were stabbing him in flank.

Bounce paraded forward, spring-footed and silent, with neck out rigid and a leafy birch twig clinging to a horn. He prodded the first of the saplings in the rear, ripping white fur from his flag, and when he stepped back to prance he had blood on his tines. Stung by pain and fury the young buck disengaged to face him, and they met head to head in orthodox attack. Freed of the double pressure, and bleeding from many holes in his hide, the switch-horn forced himself off the tree, and bounded away through the beeches with the second buck in pursuit. The young buck barked as he chased. Soon they were beyond hearing and Bounce was alone with his single opponent.

With hog-grunts and hisses they feinted and parried. They clicked antlers, stepped away, buckled their knees, and lunged forward—and Bounce took the sapling in the throat; struck him and pushed on, dirking as he pushed, carrying him backwards with his hind cletts churning the beech-leaf mould. With such an advantage he pushed the attack with merciless savagery, till the sleek satin neck was ruffled and bleeding, and the two-year-old was down on his flag and over on his back. For a fleeting moment he was like an overturned beetle, kicking on air. In that moment Bounce stabbed down to pin him to the ground, and his antlers raked heaving ribs, furrowing to the bone. The young buck flailed with his forehooves. He wriggled on his back. A hoof-stroke struck Bounce's jaw, cutting skin and stouning; his head went up. The prong-horn rolled on his side and, struggling to his feet, fled into the thickets. For a hundred yards Bounce followed him, barking as he bounded. Then he stopped to thrash in the brush, and rub his wound against a branch, before changing direction to seek Sona in her lair.

At the far end of the wood the second prong-horn was parading as master; he had driven the switch into the heather. For three days he took charge of the switch's followers, and his power was unchallenged. They were days of warm sun and soft winds, and in the clear caller dawn Bounce and Sona played their love-game on the ring, with dew on their legs and the heather sparkling. They raced while One Eye *croo-ed* himself to sleep and woodcock, owl-like, flitted into cover for the day. Then the switch came back to the wood. . . .

For a day after his defeat he had roamed over farms to the west of Glencryan—morose, truculent, unpredictable in the cold fury of defeat. He had driven sheep into corners like a rioting dog; he had harassed and straddled terrified yearling heifers in a small, fenced meadow; and he had hustled a lumbering dairy cow to a burn, where she almost drowned when she stumbled in a pool. Single dogs had coursed him, but he had turned on them, freezing their will to fight. At dusk, the heifers were herded into sheds and dairy cows bedded in the byre; and at peep of day farmers prowled with guns loaded and cocked. But the switch did not return to the fields. He foxed back to Glencryan, where he rested for a day. Then, moving stealthily, without thrashing or barking, he found the prong-horn off guard, dallying with his doe. He attacked with the old craft and rediscovered savagery, and drove him from the wood.

Bounce was licking Sona's neck in a heather clearing when the switch stalked from the trees. They were on the switch's stamping ground. Bounce knew it, and was prepared to skirmish clear. But the old buck was set for war; afire with new confidence and old courage. He was coming on to challenge, with neck level and raw sores on his ribs. Bounce saw a threat to his overlordship. The glitter came to his eyes; the spring to his knee. The switch came on, stiff-legged, mincing. Bounce stamped twice and, laying flat his ears, stalked out to meet him.

They met among the purple moor grass, with the sun in their eyes and the far cries of gulls and grouse and plover in their ears. Sona turned away, calling up her fawn. The bucks touched antlers, circled head to head, buckled, and pushed. Feinting in a recoil, Bounce lunged forward again with all his strength. The switch's puny spikes could not hold him off. He stabbed once; only once. A snap like a dry stick broken—and the switch was sagging. His legs folded under him. He fell with a thud, and rolled on his side, kicking feebly. Blood was trickling into one of his eyes. Bounce kept his head low, but did not follow through; he was sick with a sudden pain in his skull. The switch quivered a forehoof and was still. A blowfly found the blood on his eye and alighted, rubbing its legs. Bounce raised his head, slowly, almost wearily. The top tine—the long ivory dirk—was missing from his right antler. It was embedded in the switch's brain. . . .

Bounce stood still, in a daze. The beech leave rustled like dragonfly wings, and a tremor ran through the wood. The moor grass yielded to the wind, drawing down the skylight, and was shot with purple. A crow yarred suddenly in the wood and Bounce turned away, blinking in the sun's level rays.

He was master of Glencryan.